C000279060

The Mating and Whelping of Dogs

Captain
R. Portman-Graham
L.D.S., R.C.S. (Eng.)

Revised by Trevor Turner, B. Vet. Med., MRCVS

POPULAR DOGS
London Melbourne Auckland Johannesburg

Popular Dogs Publishing Co. Ltd

An imprint of Century Hutchinson Ltd

Brookmount House, 62–65 Chandos Place, Covent Garden,
London WC2N 4NW

Century Hutchinson Australia (Pty) Ltd
PO Box 496, 16–22 Church Street, Melbourne,
Victoria 3122

Century Hutchinson New Zealand Limited
PO Box 40–086, Glenfield, Auckland 10

Century Hutchinson South Africa (Pty) Ltd
PO Box 337, Bergvlei, 2012 South Africa

First published 1954
Reprinted 1958, 1961, 1964, 1967, 1969, 1971, 1973, 1975, 1978, 1983
Revised edition 1986
Copyright © R. Portman-Graham 1954
Revisions and chapter 15 copyright © Popular Dogs 1986

Set in 10/11 Times Roman

Printed and bound in Great Britain by
Redwood Burn Limited, Trowbridge, Wiltshire.

British Library Cataloguing in Publication Data

Portman-Graham, R
  The mating and whelping of dogs.
  — Rev ed.
  1. Dogs — Breeding
  I. Title   II. Turner, Trevor
  636.7'082   SF427.2

ISBN 0 09 164781 9

Contents

Part I
The Service

Simple explanation of the anatomy of the reproductive organs of dog and bitch—Biological processes of mating—Period of ovulation; signs and symptoms of ovulation; its duration—Period of readiness for mating—Some general considerations: (*a*) Regarding the bitch: when a bitch can be first mated; how frequently she may be mated; when mating should cease. (*b*) Regarding the dog: when a dog should first be trained to stud work; extent to which a dog should be used; age up to which a dog may be used—Practical application of anatomical knowledge

Responsibilities of the owner of the bitch and the stud dog owner; the obligations of each to the other—Accommodation for bitch—Preparation of a mating room and its equipment—Arrival and return of bitch—Fixing the date—Mode of despatch of bitch—The travelling box—Labels—Sanitary and hygienic condition of the bitch—Number of matings

Idiosyncrasies in the behaviour of a dog or bitch at mating time—Stud dog behaviour—Reactions of the bitch—When necessary to muzzle the bitch; procedure

Methods of effecting a mating—The natural mating—The assisted mating; single-handed, and with two assistants—The table method—The hitching-post method—The 'guided' or forcible mating

Part II
Whelping

Illustrations

Foreword

by Winnie Barber
Canine Liaison Officer, The Animal Health Trust

I HAVE read in this book so much wisdom and so much sound advice that I readily commend it to all who own a kennel and especially to those who are about to start one.

The book's greatest value lies in that it sets out in simple language the difficulties that can and do crop up, first with mating and secondly with whelping.

Captain Portman-Graham very wisely believes that the most intricate details are necessary to put the picture over; the infinite pains he has been to show his wish to help not only the owner of the stud dog and brood bitch, but, and to my mind of much more importance, the dogs themselves. So much pain can be avoided by simple knowledge.

I commend, too, the fact that the author stresses the importance of calling in a veterinary surgeon in the case of the whelping bitch if there seems to be delay or any unusual symptoms.

The whole volume is made so readable as for the most part it is the result of personal experience in the author's kennel. My own experience covers Scottish Terriers, Sealyham Terriers, West Highland White Terriers, Fox Terriers and Airedale Terriers. I have been through those same scenes in all these breeds and know the value of being able to act in emergencies. This work can be equally useful to the owners of medium-sized and large breeds, as for the smaller varieties in which the experience was gained.

I think that every breeder will be the better equipped by the possession of this book.

Acknowledgement

My very sincere thanks are tendered to the artist, Miss A.J. Arnott, for the excellence of her sketches (Figures 3 and 5 to 9), and her clever perception of the suggestions I offered. I expected diagrammatic illustrations; instead, works of art have been produced, which indicate more clearly than could any photograph the details I particularly wished to be emphasized.

Such life-like delineation combined with sympathetic artistry is the work of a genius and a true dog lover. I cannot more adequately express my gratitude.

R. P. G.

Author's Preface

HAVING set out to write a book with a definite motive, it is gratifying to find that its object has been achieved.

My aim was first to invite breeders, particularly newcomers, to study carefully two important practical aspects of breeding. Secondly, I expressed confidence that breeders, by increasing their knowledge, could spare their bitches pain during a service and at whelping time; that further they could save the lives of whelps, and finally reduce the bitch mortality rate at parturition, while relieving themselves of anxiety.

Critics have expressed the view that such a book is a necessity and that its contents would be beneficial to breeders. The technical references have been endorsed by the veterinary profession, confirming that the biological facts and anatomical details are authentic.

I have received quite considerable private correspondence from breeders, complete strangers to me, who have sent me interesting accounts of their whelping experiences. A second edition affords me the opportunity of expressing satisfaction that the book has been of some help since so many have expressed in similar terms the following remarks which I quote verbatim: 'My bitch had rather a difficult whelping being a maiden, but I followed out your instructions and am glad to say I saved every whelp.' ... 'I am only a novice and this was my first litter, but I had previously read your book, sat with it in my lap during the whole evening, and everything went off quite all right exactly as you described it would, but I was thankful I had it beforehand.'

When a book is reprinted the author is given the opportunity of bringing it up to date. However, the laws of nature, the facts of life, and biological mechanism are all much as they were in the Garden of Eden. But the march of knowledge has over the years brought to light certain additional factors which I think will give added value to the subject matter and these with advantage can be discussed here.

The first concerns the circumstance when it seems completely impossible to effect a mating. This is due to the frigidity of the bitch, and results from an anatomical structure in the vagina. This is a band of voluntary muscle which plays a big part in acceptance of the dog by the bitch, ease of penetration by the dog, and finally in the tie. It is erroneously considered by many breeders that only the dog is responsible for the tie, whereas in fact the bitch has an important rôle.

When a frigid bitch will not relax this muscle the condition is often mistaken by breeders for a stricture. I suggest the only practical remedy for this difficult mating problem calls for much more patience. All hope of 'getting the job over in half an hour' must be given up. The bitch may have to be kept for two or three days to become thoroughly acquainted with the dog; her apprehension and nervousness causing her to tighten the voluntary muscle to exclude the dog, must be overcome. It is the occasion when a union will only result from a 'love match', since a mating will not be effected while the bitch remains frigid. With patience, she will ultimately relax; or in 'doggy parlance' we must be prepared to spend a considerable time until 'she warms up to her job' and voluntarily loosens the tight muscular band. If inability to effect a mating is very prolonged, it is a case where examination by a veterinary surgeon can be sought, to ascertain whether the difficulty is due to this muscular band, or whether there is in fact a definite pathological stricture or an adhesion from a previous whelping. There is a frequently confused similarity between the two conditions.

A humorous comment has been made regarding Figure 5, and I am asked how the whelp, still enclosed in foetal membrane with the placenta neatly attached, has managed to propel itself so far from the point of arrival. The answer is of course that the illustration is a line drawing, and while being exquisitely executed by the artist, it is purely diagrammatic and therefore more explanatory than any photograph could be—even if it were possible to photograph this phase at the right moment. It never occurred to me, however, that anyone would think that the whelp had walked there. I am informed that I refer to the posterior presentation, i.e. hindlegs first, as a breech presentation, where the rump is presented but hindlegs are carried forward. Although the latter is abnormal it does occur with some frequency. As it results so often in very slow delivery, I deemed it advisable, particularly for a novice's benefit, to describe in detail the assistance which can be given.

Another controversial point is that I have followed tradition in asserting that it is both unkind and unwise to breed from a bitch at every season. One must agree that it is generally accepted as a biological principle that the exercise of any function encourages and develops that function, and to mate regularly is considered good practice in other forms of livestock breeding. For example, the pig-breeder is always advised to have a sow mated at the first heat after weaning her piglings, which occurs within a few days, and it is conceded that a normal bitch has a rest of at least two months after leaving her litter. I maintain, however, that dogs are domesticated animals, that this book was written as advice to breeders of pedigree show dogs, and, apart from the affection they have for their charges, they also have to keep them in condition for exhibition for many months each year. In short, our dogs are not pigs. Strictly in accordance with scientific biological principles therefore, readers are now informed that the practice of mating their bitches at every season is not harmful. But if I am perhaps too dogmatic in saying this practice is cruel, I cannot retract the general advice I have given on the point in as far as it affects show dogs.

A minor comment is to the effect that this book might scare a novice contemplating breeding and perhaps deter him from his intention. I take an opposite view (now justified by letters actually received from beginners), and aver that a completely ignorant beginner can reasonably be apprehensive on occasions, while one who has been intelligent enough to gain knowledge beforehand will acquire a degree of confidence which will overcome any possibility of 'jitters'. If a prospective breeder is so squeamish or timid as to be put off by reading a simple explanation of a project he proposes to undertake, I suggest, in the interest of his bitch, it would be preferable for him not to breed, and instead to grow carnations. Remember that the big majority of whelping cases are normal, cause no anxiety and are happy and interesting events for owner and dog, drawing them mutually closer together. The normal whelping process must, however, be understood. I have urged that an owner should know how to recognize conditions when a case is *not* going to be normal; I designed the book to give him that ability.

October 1957 R. P. G.

I had not allowed for the advances of modern science when stating in this earlier Preface that biological processes are not subject to change and call for no revision. There is now a contraceptive pill for bitches due in season*. This is good, since it prevents any unwanted pregnancies from accidental matings, and the frustrations resulting from a misalliance. The fact that further impressions have become necessary indicates that more and more newcomers to dog breeding have acquired a simple and fundamental knowledge, instrumental in reducing unnecessary suffering and the bitch mortality rate at parturition, while increasing the number of live whelps delivered. Since this was the purpose of the book when originally written, it is with a sense of gratification that I find its aim is being achieved.

Dorridge, Warwickshire, March 1969 R. P. G.

*Today there are drugs available both in the form of injections and tablets which will either postpone or totally suppress a bitch's season. These drugs are useful for bitches with a heavy show schedule but obviously can only be used under strict veterinary supervision.

August 1986 T.T.

General Introduction

In contemplating writing this book the author was fired by two main motives. The first, to assist the novice with two of the most intricate practical phases connected with dog breeding—(a) the mating of a dog to a bitch, commonly known as the Service, and (b) the delivery by a bitch of her puppies, commonly known as Whelping. The second motive, to save the lives of bitches and their whelps. As a result of more practical knowledge having been acquired of the whelping phenomena it is expected that the mortality rate in bitches and amongst whelps should be very considerably reduced. At the same time one hopes that the information imparted will result in relieving the bitch of unnecessary pain and suffering before, during and after the natural biological event of parturition.

The Service and Whelping are two subjects which are closely co-related, and it is pertinent that they should be studied together in one volume. Without the correct and successful performance and conclusion of the former, the latter cannot come about. Consequently it was decided to divide this book into Part I, the Service; and Part II, Whelping. This Introduction serves to explain the author's aims with the book as a whole. Part I is prefaced separately regarding the subject of the Service, and at Part II will be found an individual preface to Whelping.

In any sphere of life's activities or occupations fundamental knowledge and wealth of detailed information of a subject will create and strengthen complete confidence in its practical application. Confidence invariably spells success, and nowhere in the various aspects of dog breeding is confidence more required than in the two phases we shall consider, particularly when an individual, single-handed, is faced with unforeseen or complicated circumstances in connection with either.

At the present time, owing to the increased and increasing popularity of dog breeding as a fascinating and profitable hobby, as a profession and as a national industry and export medium, there is an amazingly increased number of devotees and enthusiastic newcomers to dog breeding in each category. With certain aspects of this engrossing occupation newcomers are inclined to allow enthusiasm and ambition to outstrip experience. They embark on a venture of which previously they were ignorant, and for which, to ensure success, sound fundamental knowledge of details is required. It is natural, therefore, that there has been a corresponding influx of canine literature, amounting almost to a glut, from 'old hands' and new authors writing on modern lines and principles. The majority of these books are excellent and invaluable to the newcomer, and their perusal will enhance his or her prospects of success both with stock and from the financial aspect. Some lack enough experience to be authoritative for novices, some lack originality to stimulate the interest of the more expert breeders. In actual fact, *Popular Dogs Publishing Company* (by whom this book is published) have produced and are producing some outstandingly good text-books on individual breeds, written by an eminent authority in each particular breed. Such books are the main source of knowledge for newcomers to that breed, with much additional advice on many other matters of dog-lore. They are also producing books on matters of general interest for *all* breeds as distinct from breed interest only. In each breed book it is inevitable that there should be a degree of similarity. In a breed book it would not be practical for a long, detailed discourse to be entered into on any one of the facets of breeding, such as rearing, housing, mating, whelping and management generally. These subjects are usually dealt with in general terms only, to suit the breed, and though exceptionally sound throughout they are touched on only briefly. All will make a reference to whelping but none enters deeply into its intricacies, ramifications, vicissitudes or complications. Few make any reference at all to the actual conduct of the Service, yet a store of information is necessary for a novice breeder, without which he will be faced with pitfalls, disappointments, accidents and injuries (not only to the dogs, but also to himself) which, with deeper knowledge, could have been easily avoided.

With so much current literature it may reasonably be asked, 'Why any more?' The author can unhesitatingly reply (in the light of his own experiences, and in view of the elementary questions he is asked regarding the Service and Whelping)—because breed books are not sufficiently detailed; they do not tell the novice how to act for himself when necessary. Outlines need to be filled in. There is the need for a more advanced book which can act as a complement to, and amplify, the excellent though brief references to these subjects in the various breed books, and which, by diagrams, can emphasize important features. 'Advanced' does not mean highly technical phraseology or scientific references likely to lead the novice out of his depth, or bore him. It means simply that he will be taken a few stages further and, by more explicit detail, be provided with an increased fund of knowledge.

In the subject matter of this book the need has been met. Of necessity some of the matter is technical, but every effort has been made to simplify abstruse medical or veterinary terms and make them easily understood by a completely inexperienced breeder.

Anyone having the temerity to write a book for dog breeders and exhibitors should realize that he has attempted a task of no mean magnitude. He has to encompass over one hundred and thirty different breeds, whose type, anatomy and characteristics range from a Chihuahua to an Irish Wolfhound. As far as the two subjects dealt with in this book are concerned, there are certain general principles applicable to all breeds, particularly in connection with whelping. Regarding the Service, there are modifications according to breeds, and as far as possible these have been grouped and special methods mentioned for different breeds. When the novice has grasped fundamentals and general principles one can help him further only by advising him to watch a service or be present at a whelping of his own particular breed before attempting to control either on his own initiative. If this is under the supervision of an expert in his breed he should now be able more intelligently to appreciate verbal explanations.

Finally, any writer on a technical subject should have specialized knowledge qualifying him to do so. The author's professional work, combined with a life-long love of dogs, of which the last twenty-five years have been continuously in contact with them as a breeder, exhibitor and judge, has created a hobby of absorbing interest. The combination and culmination has been the production of this book, enabling one to pass on to others the fruits of hard experience. Its chief claim to originality is simplification of veterinary anatomical factors and biological processes, making them more easily intelligible and so ensuring confidence in their practical application. At the same time it is hoped it will inculcate in all breeders, new or old, a high esteem for the veterinary surgeon to whom their gratitude is due.

At this juncture it is essential to impress upon the reader that there is no reason for a novice to be discouraged from becoming a breeder because this book discloses that there are certain pitfalls and difficulties to be expected with the service, and teaches him how to cope with them. Similarly with whelping; the fact that sundry complications are described should not deter a keen newcomer from proceeding with his plans. In all normal circumstances a whelping case is a particularly fascinating, interesting and happy event for the owner, and a natural one for the bitch. But don't let us be ostriches and blind ourselves to the fact that whelping cases are not *always* normal or simple. One will not go so far as to say that the management of a service can be as pleasurable as a normal whelping but it certainly is not devoid of interest; and with knowledge many services are managed with the utmost ease. But it would be foolish to delude a novice into imagining that he will never experience trying and untoward situations.

Is dog breeding too specialized; should enthusiastic amateurs be discouraged? The possibility of a newcomer being deterred from taking up dog breeding as a result of the detailed information given on these two subjects has been considered. Actually, several eminent breeders of various breeds were approached as to the advisability of imparting such information. The general opinion was that it would be beneficial. The author holds the view that some newcomers tend to drop out of the game, and thus are a loss to dogdom, if at a very early stage in their breeding careers they are completely discouraged by some unforeseen occurrence connected either with the Service or with Whelping. Had such beginners had some pre-knowledge of the subject, the contingency which deterred them would have been anticipated and not have taken them unawares. Confidence, based on information gleaned from prior reading, would quite possibly have *prevented* the happenings which put them off. At least it would have reduced their significance and enabled the beginners to tackle their difficulties. They would be far more likely to continue with their hobby when in a position to surmount an early snag instead of 'falling at the first hurdle' because of ignorance. Cure of such ignorance is the purpose of this book.

Controversy is more stimulating than dogma, since it creates an added interest. It will be for the novice reader himself, and the dog-breeding public in general, to draw their own conclusions, remembering that it is not only the interests of owners which have been considered but also the welfare of the bitch, her progeny and the stud dog.

R. P. G.

Hampton-in-Arden
1954

Part I

The Service

Preface

It is a common fallacy to consider that all that is necessary for a dog to serve a bitch, and to obtain a litter of puppies, is just to put them together somewhere and expect that a mating will automatically take place. Nothing could be further from the actual facts. The majority of matings are straightforward, some are difficult, a few are extremely difficult, and in rare cases failure and complete inability to effect a mating will result. Experienced breeders with memories of some exceptionally arduous services will readily agree that the novice owner of a stud dog has a great deal to learn. He will find in the following pages all the reasons why the service cannot always be the simple, automatic act he may have thought it was. He will learn how complications and setbacks can arise, and, more importantly, he will be instructed in various methods by which difficulties can be overcome, and told of measures whereby he can prevent injury to the dog or the bitch or possibly to himself.

Let us imagine an example of a sequel to 'novice's luck'. There have been several instances of the latter in almost all breeds during the post-war years. (Incidentally, such instances do tend to quash that erroneous, unsporting impression that only experts win; many recent examples have proved that if a novice has a really good dog he gets an equal chance in competition with experienced exhibitors.) A man decides he would like to have a dog. He gets a dog pup and a knowledgeable person tells him it is a top-ranking specimen and he ought to show it. Thrilled at the prospect, he does so with marked success. He is getting caught in the vortex of the dog game and his increasing zeal takes him to his first Championship Show. Very shortly he wins a Challenge Certificate, then another, then another, and with a dizzy head he finds he owns a Champion Dog. He had previously never seen a service and the extent of his knowledge of stud work was that he knew some dogs are dogs—that is, males—and some are bitches—that is, females. While his dog's rapid rise to eminence was in progress shrewd heads had made the mental note: 'When such-and-such bitch comes into season next I'll use that dog for her.' The result: one day he receives a telegram telling him that a bitch will shortly visit his dog. Earlier, and before getting his 'third', he may have rashly advertised his dog in glowing terms and at a large fee in the jargon he had observed in the canine Press. Puffed with justifiable pride at the honour done him by receiving such a valuable bitch from a Kennel with such a reputation, he collects the bitch from his station. Nonchalantly he opens the hamper on the lawn, a bitch leaps out and (the gate of course being left open) streaks down the lane. After a cross-country run and hue-and-cry on foot, or by exceeding the speed limit in his car through the streets of a town, he is eventually lucky enough to retrieve the bitch. She promptly, and quite rightly, bites him. This is only his first bite, and only a few drops of sweat have so far been shed. More are to come. It never occurred to him to take a collar and lead, but someone who helped to catch the bitch lent him some rope with which this valuable bitch was reluctantly and in undignified manner dragged back. Home again, and this time quite pointedly securing the gate, the service barometer starts to rise. With 'do or die', 'now we will get on with the job at once', expressions he drags an extremely frightened, very snappy and unhappy bitch into a shed. This being cluttered up with garden paraphernalia and a collection of obsolete household utensils, but devoid of a table or a chair or a strip of matting, straw or any sacking, it was inevitable that the bitch, on release from her rope lasso, should dash away and get entangled with the lawnmower in her endeavour to hide behind something. Note that it never struck our enthusiast to realize that the bitch had had a long and frightening train journey, and might be thirsty and hungry, and would probably be very scared after finding herself running in a panic in strange surroundings. These discomforts would so easily have been allayed by the humane thought of postponing an attempt at operations for two or three hours, at once putting the bitch in a warm bed of straw or wood wool with a hot drink and food by her. Having observed her highly strung state, the addition of a sedative to the drink would have settled her down. Again, it was an oversight not to have ascertained her pet or Kennel name, use of which might have induced a more friendly approach; instead, and being unaccustomed to being addressed as 'Come here, you bitch!', she naturally would try to jam herself behind the garden roller for added seclusion, and snap at any attempt to dislodge her. 'Perhaps she will come out if I bring the dog in,' thought the stud manager (what a hope!) as he promptly went to fetch the latter, with a self-satisfied expression of dawning intelligence as he remembered to secure the door as he left. The young dog, with no sexual experience whatsoever (being the sole dog owned), when brought in (loose) to the shed sniffs appreciatively and in some uncanny way senses something entirely new has occurred in his short, sweet life and, from his expression, something that promises to be interesting and full of fun. He espies the bitch (now trying to get still farther behind the roller) and as it dawns on him that she is responsible for all his excitement, what more natural than for him to run quickly, playfully and joyfully to greet her on the other side? For this boldness he receives a really nasty bite on the end of his nose. He would have received many more elsewhere, had he not retired as quickly as he made his advances. Sudden ardour is diminished; what seemed likely to be enjoyable didn't seem to be so funny after all, and more attention is being paid to his nose end, now bleeding copiously, as he mournfully paws it. (Of course there was nothing at hand to staunch it.) The stud manager, a little more nonplussed, decides that some sort of next move is obviously up to him; he must forcibly drag the bitch from her hiding-place and try firmness to induce her to begin the performance of the object of her visit. Striding determinedly towards her, and treading on a rake whose handle gave him a whack on the forehead, he makes a grab at the bitch's scruff, and receives another painful bite. To have put on a pair of thick leather gardening gloves was quite beyond his perception. Though decrying his lack of preparedness, one can but admire his dogged determination and resourcefulness, born of 'unnecessary' necessity. His next move was to throw an old rope potato-net over her head with one hand and forcibly pull her out by the tail with his other; the dog meanwhile being too peeved over his bloody nose to take much further interest in the proceedings.

After a struggle and one or two more minor bites, the rope net was wound round the bitch's head to serve as a crude muzzle. Thereafter all three parties seemed a little happier; the owner felt more secure, the bitch became more docile and the dog, realizing that he had nothing more to fear from the head end, renewed his investigations of the other. Whereupon the bitch promptly sat down, and any attempt to make her stand on her hind legs merely induced her to roll over on her back. It was fortunate that her intended mate was only a shy young dog; a sour old veteran stud has been known to bite a bitch for this perverseness. Our youngster merely sat back looking very puzzled and sheepish. The owner's grim determination was not exhausted; perhaps straddling her and gripping her between the knees would keep her upright? She resignedly succumbed to such force. Meanwhile, the dog was several yards away and now would not act on his own initiative. By dint of much patient coaxing he did approach, and a tentative mounting was essayed. But the owner was so inexperienced that it only dawned on him slowly that perhaps it would have been advisable to have had assistance from another person, that is, one to attend to the dog and one to attend to the bitch. After alternately helping dog and bitch, but finding that on releasing the one the other did everything he did not want it to do, the owner's dilemma reached its climax. His exertions from the time he opened the travelling box had been continuous for two-and-a-half hours, and he was just about where he started. He did not want the bitch's owner to have the extreme disappointment of losing the season by no mating, he did not want to lose his first fat fee, and he did not want to be a subject for ridicule. Consequently, with increasing perspiration from both physical and psychological turmoil, and somewhat bloodstained, by his own blood and that of both dog and bitch, he now resorts to the telephone, requesting advice from an experienced breeder who, fortunately, was not too distant from him. To his unbounded relief the breeder, as is typical of the *camaraderie* in the dog game, replied that he would come over right away. On hearing the sad story, he took a quick glance at the bitch's vulva, and his instructions were crisp. 'She'll hold all right till tomorrow. Make her a warm bed, leave a hot drink and a good meal beside her. Here is a sedative to put in her drink. Keep her quiet and keep the dog as far away from her sleeping-place as possible. Have a stiff whisky-and-soda yourself. I'll be along at nine in the morning and fix things up for you.'

And so a disillusioned young stud dog went back to his kennel, thinking that this was just not his idea of love at first sight, and deciding that after all he preferred his bones.

Many of the various ways in which the experienced breeder could and did 'fix things up' the next morning will be gleaned from the ensuing chapters. The owner retired that night not feeling too happy, but the next night, after things had been satisfactorily fixed up, he was a less sad though very much wiser man. One could go on elaborating indefinitely, but we will draw a veil over further quandaries which might have occurred had our novice, single-handed, reached the stage of an actual union. The foregoing facetious episode is not, however, without a basis of truth. One has heard of practically all the situations at some time or another, from novices who have sought assistance when unable to achieve the desired result on attempting the first service for their dog. The narrative was concocted to show also that an earlier statement— that the owner of a stud dog has a lot to learn—was not an exaggeration. This will be appreciated if the reader will refer back and count the number of actions which should, or should not, have taken place. He will find that even in the few pages of this preface no fewer than twenty tips and wrinkles have been given. Knowledge of these would either have prevented the *débâcle* or certainly would have eased many of the situations.

When the reader has finished this book he will find that the number of similar pieces of advice regarding the service will have reached considerably more than three figures!

Why is it that, among all the canine literature available detailed instructions on orchestrating the actual act of sexual union or even a description of the anatomy concerned appears but infrequently? Without this fundamental knowledge it is obvious that no breeder, particularly a novice, can manage a service to the best advantage or effectively meet and overcome the various difficulties which can occur.

The writer has come to the conclusion that the lack of instruction on this subject is due to its delicate nature—that is, to a form of mock modesty. He considers such a view foolish; we live in an enlightened age, and the Victorian era has long passed. If a man or woman takes up dog breeding as a hobby or a profession, the management of the service is an important part of that occupation; details should be studied and knowledge gained in the same way that intimate knowledge has to be acquired in the nursing, medical or veterinary professions. Consequently he has decided to get down to brass tacks and facts, and in Chapter I will be found information considered essential. The matter is discussed with discretion, but no detail has been omitted, either in that chapter or subsequent ones, if inclusion was deemed likely to be valuable. Many of the details are mentioned in order that the prospects of a young and valuable stud dog shall not be impaired by mishandling during its earlier experiences. Many details will concern the bitch, to ensure her comfort and diminish any possibility of pain at the time of her union.

Connected with the carrying out of a service there are certain responsibilities of the stud dog owner to the owner of the bitch, and *vice versa*. Attention to small details will enable arrangements to be conducted smoothly and brought to a harmonious conclusion for both parties. These matters are discussed in Chapter 2.

As to the management of the actual union of the dog and bitch, the first thing to be learnt is the impossibility of expecting hard and fast rules to be laid down, or to expect that every service is managed in the same way. It is for this very reason that some treatise on the subject is so necessary. Stud dogs have their own individual techniques, and these can be classified according to their individual behaviour. Equally, perhaps more, numerous are the peculiarities of bitches, which vary according to circumstances. In Chapter 3 an attempt has been made to review the contingencies which may result from the mannerisms of individual dogs and bitches at mating time.

Again, there is no cut and dried METHOD for managing any service; variations are adopted and adapted entirely according to circumstances. Some of these are due to the idiosyncrasies dealt with in Chapter 3. Many are due to the position of the owner, that is, whether he must manage alone or can rely on a second person to assist. Thus, methods can be divided into: the natural or love mating; the single-handed assisted mating; the assisted mating by two persons; and specialized methods according to breeds, such as the table mating, when very frequently manipulative assistance is given, which can be termed the 'guided' mating. Occasionally when the last method becomes imperative it is termed a 'forcible' mating. In Chapter 4 each method is explained in detail. It should be remembered that in all the methods described, apart from natural mating, a certain degree of pressure is involved and if there is undue resistance either on the part of the dog or the bitch, the 'service' should be discontinued, since 'organised' matings frequently result in subsequent problems.

Chapter 5 deals with unwritten laws regarding the financial relations between the stud dog owner and the owner of the bitch; they can be termed 'recognized customs and usages', and some affect the reputation of the owner of the stud dog for straight dealing. Their observance will enhance his chances of success as a breeder, and his Kennel reputation. Many old-fashioned proverbs are sound even though hackneyed. An example is, that in all life's ramifications honesty is ultimately the best policy; applied to dogdom there could be no greater truth. With many dog transactions, particularly those including stud work, pedigrees or the actual result of a service, it is easy to cheat. Reflect, however, that it is equally easy for the other party to realize that he has been 'done' and, smarting under an injustice, he will spread the news like a prairie fire. Any trivial, immediate gain by some petty deception, or act of actual dishonesty, is immeasurably outweighed by subsequent loss, since it calls up another old truism, 'Once bitten, twice shy.' An owner, or a Kennel, with an impeccable reputation not only gains respect from novice and expert alike, which no one can shake, but is also the one whose stud dog, or dogs, will be recommended, and whose stock is in greatest demand. Straightness ensures success; fiddling means failure.

The importance of keeping complete records of stud work is underlined in Chapter 6, where the nature of such records is explained.

A preface is usually brief. This one has intentionally been long since it might have been argued that nothing not already known could be written about the service. If, however, in this *résumé* either the novice or the expert has found reference to some fact new to him, then perusal of the book will be worth while.

Chapter 1

Simple explanation of the anatomy of the reproductive organs of dog and bitch—Biological processes of mating—Period of ovulation; signs and symptoms of ovulation; its duration—Period of readiness for mating—Some general considerations: (*a*) Regarding the bitch: when a bitch can be first mated; how frequently she may be mated; when mating should cease. (*b*) Regarding the dog: when a dog should first be trained to stud work; extent to which a dog should be used; age up to which a dog may be used—Practical application of anatomical knowledge.

SUBSEQUENT pages will indicate that it is usually preferable for a human to be present at the mating of a pedigree dog to a pedigree bitch. Further, it is certainly highly desirable in some circumstances that actual assistance be given at the service. No breeder can adequately render such assistance unless he has a fundamental knowledge of the anatomy, construction and mechanism of the reproductive organs of each sex. Similarly, in Part II (Whelping) knowledge of the anatomical situation of the bitch's generative organs will assist an owner in many aspects of this phenomenon, particularly if intervention in an emergency proves imperative. In both cases the owner with a pre-knowledge of this subject can more easily understand expressions used by a veterinary surgeon.

The Dog

The testicles contained in the scrotum are two in number (see page 20). These manufacture or secrete the seminal fluid containing innumerable spermatozoa which are the sperm cells or male seed. This fluid is conducted *via* a cord to the actual male organ, the penis, in the anterior part of which is a bone, varying in length from half an inch to four inches according to breed. In all ordinary circumstances the organ is protected by a sheath of skin, technically called the prepuce, loosely attached at the the bulb and front end. The only parts of the penis to which a stud dog owner's attention should be drawn are: the front part, composed of erectile tissue ending in a fine pointed end; and behind this a rounded bulb also composed of erectile tissue. It is due to this latter structure that in mating the phase known as the tie is brought about. This is of importance to the stud manager. From the bulb two large veins pass on to the back of the penis, where also are situated two muscles near the bulb. The purpose of this mechanism is threefold. Firstly, sexual excitement brings into operation the erectile nature of the two parts of the penis, thus enabling them to negotiate and penetrate the female passage. Secondly, sensory frictional nerve impulses induce the ejection of the fluid at the extreme end of this passage. Thirdly, the muscles referred to strongly and simultaneously compress the veins mentioned, causing them to become engorged in the bulb. The bulb when inside the female passage becomes so extremely congested and swollen as to cause the external structure of the female passage to be completely locked round it. This swollen condition of the bulb may persist for periods ranging from two minutes to one hour. The dimensions of the swollen bulb are remarkable. A comparison which may help the complete novice to visualize it is to compare it with a medium-sized, hard tomato, in small breeds up to 12 lb. There is an increase in size in proportion to the size of breeds.

Mention has been made of possible injury to a dog or a bitch. THIS LARGELY OCCURS OWING TO THE TIE, for which reason a detailed description has been given.

It should further be noted that the organ remains entirely flexible. While in the position described above, and ejaculation is taking place, the dog can and should be faced in the entirely opposite direction. The reasons for this will be described in later chapters. The method is colloquially known as 'turning' the dog.

When only one testicle has at puberty descended into the scrotum the animal is popularly known as a monorchid. Strictly this refers to an animal that is only born with one testicle. In the majority of cases these monorchids are unilateral cryptorchids, the other testicle having failed to descend and still being retained in the abdomen. Subjected to the higher temperature within the body cavity, this retained testicle carries a much higher risk of developing a tumour. In addition, the normal sex hormones produced by the testes can be produced in greater quantity by the retained testes and thus unacceptable male characteristics such as aggression and hypersexuality can be more frequent in dogs with an undescended testicle. Most authorities agree that there is an inherent predisposition to the condition, so that cryptorchid dogs should not be used for breeding.

Kennel Club breed standards state in every case that 'male animals should have two apparently normal testicles fully descended into the scrotum.'

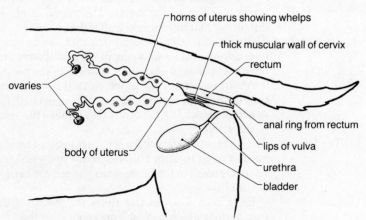

body of uterus is approximately one third the length of the vagina

Figure 1 The bitch's reproductive organs

A true monorchid like an anorchid that is born without any testicles, is an extremely rare condition. If both testicles fail to descend, the animal is strictly a bilateral cryptorchid, although popularly called cryptorchid. Obviously cryptorchids whether unilateral or bilateral i.e. monorchid or cryptorchid (to use popular jargon), should not be bred from.

The Bitch

The genitals of the bitch are:

(a) Externally: The vulva, which is the external opening of the urino-genital system and consists of a pair of lips joined top and bottom. A small knoblike structure, called the clitoris, composed of erectile tissue (and correspond-ing to the penis in the dog), which provokes for the bitch the acceptance of the dog, is found just within the vulval lips.

(b) Vagina: Although popularly known as the vagina, it is the vestibule that leads from the vulva as far as the opening of the urethra or female urinary passage. The vestibule is thus a common urino genital passage and contains very strong muscle fibres which play a part during the 'tie' when dog and bitch are joined during service.

    The vagina proper extends from the external urethral orifice to the cervix. The vagina is highly distensible and lies entirely within the pelvis.

(c) The Cervix: This is an extremely muscular structure which relaxes only during heat to allow the passage of sperms and during whelping to allow the expulsion of the puppy.

    A narrow central canal, the cervical canal, which runs through the cervix, connects the vagina with the womb or uterus. It is the cervix that is called the 'neck of the womb'.

(d) The Uterus: The entire womb is pearshaped with a pair of uterine horns joining to form a single uterine body which is relatively small in the bitch, since puppies are carried in the horns.

    Each horn is about five times the length of the uterine body which is in itself only about one third the length of the vagina, hence the reason that the vagina of the bitch is often referred to as being long.

The special mucous membrane lining the womb is called the endometrium and the muscle layer is the myometrium.

The uterine horns run forward on each side of the abdomen and are relatively straight, ending at the ovary which produces the eggs which, when fertilized by spermatozoa, result in the foetuses growing ultimately into puppies.

As the uterine horns proceed towards the ovaries they become smaller and are known as Fallopian tubes. These are only attached to the ovary by connective tissue which surrounds the ovary and the Fallopian tubes. Eggs shed by the ovary are caught by the Fallopian tubes and are passed down into the horns of the uterus.

Having discussed the anatomy or description of the structures we must now look at the physiology which is a description of the function of these organs. Very briefly the ovaries produce eggs during oestrus or heat and these pass down the Fallopian tubes into the horns of the womb. Normal period between seasons or heat is six months but this can vary from as short a time as three to four months up to a year or even more.

The biological process of ovulation will be described in detail later. Provided the ova of the bitch and the sperm cells, or seed, of the dog are *both* fertile (see note below) at the time of the union a variable number of ova are 'pierced' by innumerable sperms, only one of which, however, is selected. The cells of an ovum and the cells of a sperm then undergo fission or dividing up, the whole process being known as the fertilization of the ovum. Those ova which have become fertilized attach themselves very firmly to the membranous walls of each horn of the womb. Many ova not impregnated by semen pass out as a mucous discharge subsequently. During the ensuing weeks, known as the period of gestation, further development from the two original sex cells goes on apace, their fusion forming an embryo or foetus. The period of gestation normally lasts 63 days, at the end of which the foetus is a fully developed whelp, waiting to see the light of day. Such, then, was the beginning and making of our future CC winner.

NOTE: Thanks to modern science and the advanced research work of the veterinary profession, the owner of an exceptionally fine specimen of a bitch or a dog, perhaps a Champion, need no longer suffer the disappointment of finding either that she is a non-breeder, i.e. non-fertile, or that he is impotent as a sire. Similarly with bitches who either fail to come into season at all, or ovulate very irregularly, going for very long periods beyond the normal six months. These disappointing inadequacies can be rectified. Hormones can now be injected to bring about ovulation; another type of hormone injection will increase the number of ova as also their fertility. Thus theoretically a litter can now be made possible and its size increased. Again, with a dog which has been used at stud, say on four occasions, and at each no litter has resulted from different bitches of proved fertility, or perhaps only one puppy, it is possible for the spermatozoa to be examined microscopically and any inadequacy on the dog's part detected. In accordance with the findings, suitable hormone injection can be administered with beneficial result. This being a purely veterinary subject, it is not one within the province of this book, though it appeared advisable that the reader should be told that by recourse to veterinary treatment such disappointments can generally be avoided. In the course of the last eight years the author has had actual experience with each type, and can speak with conviction of the efficacy of the treatment.

Period of Ovulation

The occasion on which a bitch first comes into season is variable. One bitch may begin very early at five months of age, another may show no indication of sexual change until well over twelve months old. Among almost all the breeds of Eastern origin, e.g. Pekingese, Chows, Afghans, etc., maturity comes very much earlier, bitches of these breeds often starting in season at six months. As a normal average, however, the first oestrum is apparent at about ten months. Thereafter in a normal bitch it recurs with precise regularity every six months. In the periods between the seasons there is no possibility of a bitch being mated; and unless extremely highly sexed, neither the dog nor the bitch has any sexual interest for the other, and both can live together in harmony, unhampered by any sex urge and with no embarrassment for an owner.

There are, however, variations from the normal due to some glandular conditions, when some bitches either fail to come into season at all or, after an initial oestrum, will cease to do so again, or be extremely irregular. Conversely, some bitches are known to come into use much more frequently than the routine six-monthly period. (See note on p. 23.)

Signs and Symptoms of Ovulation

These are unmistakable and easily recognizable. The very earliest is an enlargement in the size of the vulva, and the first signs of a tendency for a dog to become sexually attracted to the bitch. It is an important factor for an owner to observe as it is an indication that the oestrum is imminent though not actually begun. Another sign not generally known, but definitely noted with bitches kept indoors, is that for at least a fortnight before the oestrum begins there is marked frequency in urination. An otherwise clean house bitch will constantly be falling from grace. The same condition occurs with Kennel bitches, but is not so likely to be seen by the owner. This changed condition of the vulva may persist for a day only or for several before the next definite sign appears. During this time the vulva changes from a deep red to purple colour and is hard and swollen. Following this, and at variable periods, the next sign is a discharge, rapidly turning to a very dark red blood colour and rather thick. The day this discharge occurs is of the utmost importance to the owner and the date must at once be noted. It is from this sign that the date on which the actual mating shall take place is decided. The expression is that the bitch is 'showing colour'. The period of ovulation, that is, the duration of the heat, may last anything from nine to twenty-one days, and in exceptional cases for periods of over a month; it is variable in individual bitches and it is important for an owner to make a record of the habits in this respect of each of his bitches. Normally, after the first week from the first show the vulva, although remaining very enlarged, becomes looser and the tissues much softer, while at the same time the colour of the discharge lightens and by the tenth day is usually only a faint pink, gradually disappearing and generally colourless by the fourteenth day. Another most important thing for the owner to note is that the bitch is not mateable, nor desirous of being mated, throughout the whole of this period. The term 'being ready' is applied to the time within this period when she will be willing to consort with and invite intercourse from the dog, indicating this by curling her tail from the cover it normally gives to the vulva, and quite obviously 'standing', and frequently thrusting her hind part towards any dog near her. During the whole period of oestruation a bitch causes sexual stimulation in any dog, and his desire to mate is persistent throughout, though, as has been already mentioned, this is not so with the bitch. This stimulation is induced because the discharge from the bitch has an individual smell, to which the dog is very receptive, and reacts naturally and instantly. This smell cannot be detected by human beings, so causes them no unpleasantness. It is essential, therefore, that the in-season bitch must be kept closely confined, preferably under lock and key, for a period of at least three weeks. It is unwise to keep an in-season bitch in the house if a dog also is kept indoors; the dog would be under a persistent strain likely to harm his nervous system. It is kinder to the dog for the bitch to be segregated in an outside kennel. It should have a small run, but should be completely enclosed either by boards or netting for a height of six feet, as it is remarkable how acrobatic dogs can become at this time. With the bigger breeds, for additional precaution the run should also be provided with a close-fitting roof. A bitch thus in purdah must be exercised; it is not only cruel, but also detrimental to her well-being, for her to be cut off from normal existence for the whole of the period.

To prevent the nuisance of other dogs in the neighbourhood getting scent and visiting the kennel, one can either carry the bitch for 200 yards or take it a short distance in a car, and then walk it, on a lead, in a field or other suitable place. The scent is then not followed to the kennel. Various proprietary preparations are obtainable which, if applied to the bitch's rear legs, mask the odour and deter dogs from approaching. They are quite useful when out exercising the bitch but could not be relied on to prevent a dog ultimately being attracted and effecting a mating if both were left together for any time. Despite precautions being taken, occasionally misalliances or unintentional matings do occur, either to a stray dog or to a kennel inmate not intended as the sire. In such cases consult your veterinary surgeon without delay. A contraceptive injection can be given which will abort any possible pregnancy but this must be given within a maximum of 72 hours of mating and is more reliable if given earlier. The injection is not without certain drawbacks. It will prolong heat by at least another one to two weeks and if the bitch were mated again during this period, although she would probably not become pregnant, it would be unlikely for the veterinary surgeon to repeat the injection.

There must be a popular belief, since the writer has so frequently been asked the question, that if a pedigree bitch has made an alliance with a mongrel, or dog of entirely different breed, she is ruined, and is of no further use as a breeding bitch. Such an idea is of course entirely erroneous. The resultant litter would be valueless as pedigree stock but, provided the whelps were of a size commensurate with the normal ones of the bitch's breed and did her no harm at parturition, she would at subsequent seasons be perfectly normal in all respects when mated to a pedigree dog of her own breed.

Having referred to minor factors concerning the phase when a bitch is on heat, we can now revert to the main subject. Another quite variable factor is the actual period at which a bitch is described as being 'ready' to be mated. The behaviour of the bitch at this stage of readiness has been mentioned, but duration is by no means constant with all bitches. In some cases it is only a matter of a few hours when a bitch will stand and be willing for a dog to mate her. Others will stand readily to the dog at any time during periods varying from two to six days. In exceptional cases some bitches are ready for a whole fortnight. An owner should always keep a record of the behaviour of each of his brood bitches in this respect. As a general rule it is rare for a bitch to be mateable before the ninth day, or after the fourteenth day, though extreme cases are known when a mating has been effected at the eighteenth day, with a litter resulting. In the majority of cases the eleventh day is found to be the most suitable for a bitch to be receptive to a mating. From the foregoing it will be appreciated that it is advisable to observe the bitch frequently during her season, particularly when an arrangement has been made with the owner of a stud dog for the service. If the discharge ceases early, and there are indications of the vulva shrinking and becoming smaller before the expected date (the condition being colloquially described as 'drying-up'), it will be necessary to make fresh arrangements and hasten the despatch of the bitch. This avoids the disappointment of no litter resulting, because the bitch had dried up before a mating could take place.

It should be emphasized that although a bitch may have been satisfactorily mated at the eleventh day she may remain vulnerable for several days afterwards. All precautions regarding her seclusion to prevent an indiscretion on her part must be rigidly maintained for the full twenty-one days for safety, and not ended until every trace of the oestrum has cleared. Usually, she will then herself see the dog off by snapping at it in no uncertain manner, and such a surly reception usually induces the dog to give up the contest.

Some General Considerations

(*a*) *The bitch* An aspect of breeding which may fittingly be considered in this chapter is when a bitch should be first mated and how often she should be mated. Here one can almost lay down a general rule, that if a bitch comes into season at any age before she is twelve months old it is unwise to mate her at her first season and preferable to wait till the next season, when she will be more matured in every way, physically and temperamentally. An exception is made for Miniature breeds, where whelping is generally a little more difficult than for bigger breeds, and a bitch may be mated at her first season if not earlier than nine months old. If a bitch is very late in starting her first season, and does not do so until between twelve and eighteen months of age, it is in this case in order to mate her at her first season. A bitch should not be expected to deliver puppies like a machine every time she comes into season; such a procedure is cruel and heartless and not really lucrative since both the bitch and the quality of her whelps soon deteriorate, and in the long run the practice results in loss. Owners with great love and respect for their bitches will mate them only every other season, approximately a litter a year, resting one season and mating the next. An intermediate stage, whereby a strong, healthy bitch does not suffer any deleterious effect, is to mate her twice only in three seasons; that is, if she has been allowed to have litters at two successive seasons, invariably she should be rested for the next. If a bitch has been a maiden for three or four years there is considerable risk of her having a very difficult time at whelping, even if she conceives. A bitch who has had many previous litters, and proved an easy whelper, is safe to go on mating up to the age of seven or eight years. Beyond that age it is regarded as both unwise and unkind, though one has heard of bitches producing litters comfortably when twelve years old; usually, however, the progeny degenerates.

(*b*) *The dog* We will now consider the ages and extent of the use of stud dogs within wise limits. Firstly, however, it must be impressed on the novice stud dog owner that his dog must be *trained* to his peculiar profession of combining business with pleasure. A dog who does not gain his first experience while young is usually very difficult later to make into an intelligent stud dog. A dog who has not been put to a bitch until he is, say, three to four years old will most probably have no idea of what is expected from him and fail to effect a service. The best age at which to start training a stud dog, and at which he should be introduced to his first bitch for a service, is ten months. He should not serve again for another two months, and another two months should elapse between the next service, when he should be allowed to serve not more than one bitch a month until eighteen months old. These are given as maximum intervening periods; with a robust, virile dog, after fifteen months old an occasional additional bitch would not be really detrimental, but to over-use a young dog under eighteen months is to weaken him, and if carried to excess, to ruin him, however much he is in demand or the magnitude of the fees he could earn. There is a pre-war case on record in a certain breed of an outstanding young dog whose value ran into four figures and who earned in his first year an amount not far short of four figures. To do this, however, while still so young, he was being grossly over-used, serving bitches on two, three or four successive days. He became completely worn out, and was dead before he was two years of age. A little mental arithmetic will quickly show the folly and shortsightedness of such financial greed. Had he served a third of the number of bitches in the first year, and half that number in the second, he would have earned only approximately £400, but in all probability would have lived and served and earned an increased amount for a further six years, representing at least £3,000. Thus in the long run the cruel abuse of this dog represented a loss of some £2,500 to the owner. After eighteen months of age a dog should not serve a bitch more often than once a week on an average. The fact that a dog is capable of, and willing for, more frequent services does not alter the fact that it is unsound to abuse the animal. To overstep this rule occasionally would not necessarily be detrimental, but to exceed it regularly over a period would be unwise, if the owner hopes to make the dog a lasting sire of sound, robust stock. The starting age of ten months need not be slavishly adhered to, as in special circumstances a knowledgeable dog can be used younger; ten months is quoted as the optimum age, nine or eight months are possible, younger is unwise and a result unlikely. We were, however, ourselves guilty in very special circumstances of deviating from the above advice quite recently. We had a promising dog pup only just turned seven months, when due to fulfil a commission and depart to Australia. We were particularly anxious to retain his blood line before he left us. Candidly, we never considered a result likely, but we thought we would just try him at stud on the merest offchance. To our surprise he functioned perfectly; the bitch proved in whelp and in due course delivered six puppies. We have heard that he was used in Australia about three months later (aged ten months) and another sizeable litter resulted. Apparently such an early service was not detrimental. It should be noted that the bitch to whom this exceptionally gay Lothario was mated was a proven old brood of six years. An axiom is: to an old brood bitch use a quite young dog; and let an old or ageing stud dog serve only quite young or maiden bitches. The result in progeny is generally a larger-size litter with no degeneracy. To mate a very old dog to a very old bitch is not always sound; the size of the litter is invariably diminished, and deterioration in progeny usually results. Frequently only one puppy arrives, of exceptional size and sometimes monstrous and dangerous to a bitch at whelping time. The age up to which a dog can profitably be used at stud, with prospects of the bitch owner having an honest deal and a fair prospect of a worthwhile litter, varies with individual dogs and quite definitely in individual breeds. No rule can be laid down. As a guide, it can be said that by ten years of age a stud dog has aged; if he has been used extensively and regularly over the years he would, in regard to sexual competence, be older than a dog of the same age who had been used much less. Approaching or beyond ten years, the activity of the sperms diminishes and smaller and degenerate stock can be expected. Dogs have been used at twelve years, and in extremely exceptional cases later, but a dog of twelve years is equivalent to an old gentleman of eight-four years, and though the spirit might be willing the flesh will undoubtedly have weakened. In spite of the fact that many a good tune is played on an old fiddle there are perhaps limits.

Practical Application of Anatomical Knowledge

The sole reason for describing in detail anatomical structures at the beginning of this chapter was to show the value of such knowledge when applied practically either to the supervision of a service or to various phases connected with whelping. In Part II the latter is dealt with; this chapter is concluded by advice on the practical application to a service.

With a big majority of breeders it is customary to note:

1. THE ANGLE of the vaginal passage from the vulva. The flatter this is, or more nearly horizontal, the more difficult will be its negotiation by the dog, causing a lot of unnecessary fumbling and waste of energy, and frequently calling for assistance from the manager. The steeper the angle, the easier will be penetration by the dog. Exploration of this angle will show how best the dog may be assisted, when circumstances appear to make assistance necessary, by either raising or lowering the bitch, or by giving the dog something for his hind legs to stand on. This will be more fully explained in the chapter dealing with methods.

2. THE LENGTH OF THE PASSAGE. This varies. The extent of the vagina is determined by how soon the bony brim of the pelvis is encountered. If a short passage, the pelvic bone is felt with ease; if long, the extent of a little finger (in small breeds) or the middle finger (in larger breeds) may not reach it. The longer the passage the easier and more certain will be the service and the effecting of a tie. If very short there is a tendency for a dog, after making penetration, to keep slipping out again, after only a few seconds. This is irritating, to the dog and to the manager, and is countered (immediately after penetration) by placing the hand on the dog's rump, firmly and forcefully pressing him to the bitch and maintaining contact for him. It may be necessary to keep the dog in this position for several minutes. Further, when the passage is short it is quite impossible for the large bulbular enlargement (mentioned in the anatomical description) to enter the passage and continue to enlarge therein, thus producing the tie. Its appearance, however, outside the vulva does cause consternation to the complete novice, who probably did not know of its existence, or, if he did, where it should actually be at this stage. Provided that the forward portion of the erectile part of the

penis is within the passage, and kept there by firmly holding the dog clasped to the bitch, he can be assured there is no cause for anxiety, that everything is going on satisfactorily, and that a service is being effected. Here an important question will be answered, since it is one so frequently asked. Is it necessary for a tie to be effected, and can a service be considered satisfactory and conception counted on if no tie has taken place? The answer is that it is *not* necessary for an actual tie to be effected for conception to follow, and a litter of puppies to result. Provided there has been penetration, and the penis actually remained in the vaginal passage while ejaculation was taking place, if only for a few moments and under one minute, this could be regarded as a satisfactory service, and the owner of the bitch be honestly assured that, provided both dog and bitch are fertile, a litter can be expected. The author learnt this lesson (since verified on many occasions) when himself a complete novice and using a stud dog for its first service. The dog was very raw, unintelligent and uncooperative, and half an hour had elapsed before penetration took place, the dog remaining in position for less than a minute and then slipping away. Exactly the same thing happened two or three times more. The author was nonplussed, thinking that as there had been no tie it could not be regarded as a service and no fee should be taken. Fortunately, however, the bitch's owner, who was considerably experienced, was present thoughout and had tried to assist, but did not appear to be in the least disappointed. He said he was quite satisfied that each time the dog was there for periods considerably under a minute, and one only a few seconds, a service had been given, and took the bitch away quite contentedly. The sequel—a litter of six puppies. As an example of one of the inexplicable vagaries of the service, the author has had the converse experience of a perfect mating and a firmly locked tie lasting one hour five minutes, during which all parties, human and canine, got thoroughly bored. Yet the result was a miss—no conception, no litter. For corroboration of these two extremes the author is indebted to an authoritative bulldog breeder, with two similar experiences. The first, a tie lasting three-quarters of an hour but with no puppies resulting. The second, an amazingly short period of actual penetration lasting only two seconds, the result being a record litter of twelve puppies! Having made a summary from a wide range of very diverse breeds, it can definitely be stated that the average duration of a normal service with a perfect tie is twenty minutes.

To revert to consideration of the dog immediately slipping out. By such repeated abortive efforts to penetrate, the dog will sometimes swell completely and begin to eject outside the bitch. This may cause a novice to think that the effort has been wasted, that the service cannot be accomplished, and consequently to give it up. This is not so; it can be accomplished, and consequently to give it up. This is not so; it can be countered by removing the bitch altogether, and if the dog is a short legged one holding him away from the ground to avoid contact irritation. After a few minutes the organ will retract into the prepuce. This can be accelerated by fanning with a newspaper, or applying cold water. The dog should then be returned to its kennel for half an hour.

A further attempt can be made but in such a case some assistance may be necessary. The method will be described in a later chapter.

3. DIAMETER OF THE PASSAGE. Sometimes even when ready the vulva and vagina are so small that normal mating is impossible. Dilation with the little finger repeated several times may make entrance possible and certainly helps to induce acceptance in the very shy timid bitch. More severe methods including general anaesthesia and stretching by a veterinary surgeon should not be contemplated since even if mating is effected, it is unlikely that whelping without complications will be able to take place.

4. A STRICTURE, ADHESION, OR GROWTH present in any part of the passage. This is felt as a hard obstruction to the exploring finger, beyond which it cannot go. In such a case a service is usually quite impossible. The owner of the bitch should be told and no fee should be taken as no service has taken place and there is therefore no possibility of conception. He should advise the owner to take the bitch to his veterinary surgeon for advice. This precludes any false statement a bitch owner could make to the effect that the stud dog could not mate the bitch or was not potent. In the few instances when we have found it quite impossible to effect a service, and the bitch owners have been so informed, we have been fortunate in that the veterinary surgeon has confirmed that an anatomical defect existed.

5. SOMETIMES THE BITCH IS BROUGHT TOO LATE; the vulva has tightened and is very small and the lumen (width or diameter of the passage) has diminished. Quite frequently the vulva of some bitches remains tight and small throughout the whole oestrum, although they will evince readiness. This must not be confused with (3) above, an anatomical narrowness while the bitch is still very ready in other respects, though the conditions are almost identical. By the application of Vaseline, by dilation and stimulation, a service can sometimes be managed with a tight vulva, but frequently it cannot. The owner must then be informed that no service has taken place, and the reason given. No fee is justified.

Although it has been said that many breeders make a regular routine of digital exploration for the purposes described above, many others consider it necessary only when they come up against some difficulty that makes penetration difficult or impossible.

The principles having been explained, it can now be left to the reader to discriminate, and work out his own procedure after experience. The author would sum up by saying that digital examination is by no means always necessary but is frequently highly desirable. Whenever a digital examination is made the following preliminary precautions should be taken: the nail of the finger should be cut very short, and be smooth. The finger should be thoroughly scrubbed and immersed in an antiseptic solution, e.g. dilute Dettol or T.C.P. Before insertion it should be well smeared with medicated Vaseline.

The Dog

Compared with the bitch, in the dog the presence of any anatomical abnormality of the sex organ is extremely rare; for all general purposes it may be regarded as normal. There is, however, a fact connected with the practical application which should be noted; it is the flexibility of the organ which enables the dog to be turned completely round to face the opposite direction when tied. Among breeders this is known as turning the dog. The method of carrying this out is described in a later chapter, but the following is an explanation of the reason for the procedure. It is always observed in practically all breeds, particularly those of the more aggressive types as compared with the more domesticated, that when a dog has mounted and is serving a bitch he becomes restless, fidgety, not at ease in the position, and exhibits a desire to dismount. If he does so before the bulb swells in the passage, this is a cause of the tiresome slipping out. If actually tied and a dog tries to dismount, it is one of the situations which made necessary the information that a dog can injure himself and the bitch during the service, and at which stage attention is necessary to prevent such injury. In a perfect service the lock is so firm that it is almost impossible for the dog to disengage himself; but a fractious dog endeavouring to get free will tug and struggle, to the discomfort of himself and the bitch. He must be gently but firmly restrained until the swelling has reached the maximum and the tie completed. He can then be turned, and it will be found that the restlessness ceases and both dog and bitch quieten down, each appearing to prefer this turned position and remaining steady till the service is completed.

There is a theory—and it is only a theory—to explain why a dog prefers to be turned. The dog at some time lived in the wild state. While carrying out a service, with his front legs clasping the bitch, both are completely defenceless if attacked. The instinct doubtless remains; if other dogs approached while a service was in progress they would be regarded as rivals by the dog, and at a time when he would be vulnerable to attack, as also would be the bitch. If, however, he is dismounted during the tie, and each is facing in opposite directions, each would be able to put up a fight. To what extent this theory is true is difficult to judge, but it is certainly a routine with breeders to allow the dog finally to assume the position by turning him, having found that he will then stand passively for the duration of the service. When completed, separation is simple and natural; some breeders think it advisable to hold up the bitch's hind legs for a short time to prevent the semen running out, but it is unnecessary to do so. The bitch should now be returned to her kennel and the dog led off.

Chapter 2

Responsibilities of the owner of the bitch and the stud dog owner; the obligations of each to the other—Accommodation for bitch—Preparation of a mating-room and its equipment—Arrival and return of bitch—Fixing the date—Mode of despatch of bitch—The travelling box—Labels—Sanitary and hygienic condition of the bitch—Number of matings.

AT THIS stage a digression from anatomy and intimate detail may be refreshing. Consequently, before dealing further with various methods of mating we will consider certain preliminaries which are the responsibility and the mutual obligations of the owner of the stud dog and the owner of the brood bitch.

The Stud Dog Owner

1. *Accommodation for bitch* If the establishment is a modest one of one or two dogs only, but advertises a dog at stud, or is one of the most extensive Kennels, suitable accommodation should be reserved for housing a bitch who may be a visitor for a day or two. It is advisable first to ascertain if the visiting bitch is accustomed to being indoors as a house dog or to living outside. Some owners take the trouble to allow a house bitch to be accommodated indoors in a room set apart, the door of which can be safely secured. Otherwise a separate kennel outside should be used, and permanently kept for visiting in-season bitches. It should be in some secluded spot, as distant from other dogs or bitches as possible. A small run should be attached, preferably covered in, every care being taken that there is no possible chance of the bitch getting out, or of a dog getting in. It is a prime responsibility of the stud dog owner that no *mésalliance* shall occur while the bitch is in his charge.

Fresh clean bedding, straw or wood-wool should be placed in the kennel for each new arrival. The old bedding should be burnt as soon as a bitch departs, and the kennel should be scrubbed with disinfectant. In case the bitch has left any undesirables behind it is advisable to use an insecticide.

2. *Preparation of a mating-room* The size of the room in which matings will be carried out is immaterial; generally, however, the smaller the better. An outhouse, small shed or empty garage are suitable; or the room can be used in combination with the one where grooming is usually done. Essentials are that it should be as bare as possible, and it should have good light, both artificial and from a window. The latter is useful to look through from the outside when a dog and bitch have been left alone together for a few moments in the early stages. An electric heater or some other form of heating, suitably guarded, is useful in the winter months. A secure latch, or lock and key, is essential.

3. *Equipment in the mating-room* To cover all the methods of mating described in Chapter 4 the following equipment is necessary. A table approximately 2 feet by 4 feet. Attached to this at one end it is useful to have a post into which a large staple has been driven, or an iron ring screwed in. Alternatively, if one end of the table is pushed against a wall the staple or iron ring can be fixed to the wall. This meets the requirements of the hitching-post method. One or two low stools or hassocks, or a low chair, or a bale of straw or a rolled-up rug; these are for the convenience of the assistants in the on-the-ground method. A strip of coconut mat on the floor, or other non-slip covering, for the convenience of the dog, and also a rolled-up sack to assist him when it is found necessary to raise his hind legs to a bitch much taller than he is. Other items of equipment include: Vaseline for smearing round the vulva to facilitate penetration. A strip of $1\frac{1}{2}$-inch-wide bandage from 2 to 3 feet long according to size of breed. When it does become necessary to muzzle the bitch this is by far the quickest and simplest method; its use is described later. A pair of thick leather gloves, as a precaution with an obstreperous bitch who attempts to bite. Similarly, in the exceptional case of a human being bitten some tincture of iodine, or TCP, is useful to have handy as an antiseptic before applying a dressing. A pair of scissors to cut long hair from the hind legs and in the region of the vulva in the case of long-coated breeds. (See further note on page 38.)

4. *On arrival of the bitch* As the bitch will have had a long journey delay should be minimized by either being at the station to meet her or arranging that her arrival is at once notified by telephone. Take her box straight to her kennel or isolated enclosure, use her pet name, and let her out of her box after making certain that all gates are secured and that her kennel or enclosure latch is safe. If her own isolated run is small, put a lead on, carry her some distance, then let her have a lead walk or run in a suitable spot. On return offer her a meal and a drink; if exceptionally nervous and highly strung, consultation with your veterinary surgeon regarding the advisability of sedation may be

worthwhile. Examine the vulva and decide if she must be mated the same day. If so, delay doing so till she has been bedded down for a few hours. If it is quite definite that she will hold till the next day settle her down for the night. See that any detachable gadgets for securing her travelling box are put in a safe place and not lost before she is due to return, and fasten her own lead to her travelling-box. Empty and clean her travelling box and replace fresh wood-wool or straw. By 'phone or wire inform her owner of her safe arrival.

5. *Returning the bitch* If only a short journey and her arrival was early in the morning she can sometimes be mated and returned the same day. Almost invariably, however, she is kept at least one night, possibly two or three. By 'phone or wire inform the owner of the bitch the result of the service, and give full information regarding the return journey. Dogs are frequently mislaid while travelling owing to carelessness *en route*. Consequently, the following details should be given: Time and station of departure; stations at which changes will be made and times of departure therefrom; time and station of arrival. This information helps the owner to trace a dog which does not reach its destination when expected. Exercise her before placing her in her box. Remember some dogs are poor travellers and vomit frequently if fed before a journey. Whether food should be offered or not should be discussed with the owner and depends on several factors including the length of journey. Ensure that her box is securely fastened. Write clearly on the label the name and address of owner, and it is advisable to add the owner's telephone number. If the bitch is to be called for at the station, and not delivered, state this boldly in block letters. One label at least should be fixed by drawing-pins—tie-on ones get torn off and sticky ones frequently don't stick. If you have no printed tally bearing the words, add another large label: VALUABLE DOG. DO NOT DELAY. A word of advice about bitches flown from or back to Eire. Firstly, they travel extremely well by air and are in no way upset by the experience. It is infinitely the best and quickest way; if you are not too distant from an airport the whole journey can be made in a minimum of two hours or maximum of five, while frequently cross-country journeys in England, involving changes and missed connections, can take twelve or fifteen hours. Secondly, airport officials seem to make a practice of removing a bitch from the basket; it is well-intentioned but it is disconcerting to see your in-season bitch being brought to you gaily trotting along on a lead— your heart misses a beat if you think that the collar might be loose; a bitch in strange surroundings might tug and slip it. On at least two occasions a kindly air porter has brought a bitch to us walking on its lead, and in Dublin it seems the common practice. To obviate this we now add yet another label for bitches travelling by air: PLEASE DO NOT

REMOVE DOG FROM TRAVELLING-BOX, EXCEPT IN EXTREME EMERGENCY.

In air travel no wood-wool or straw is allowed in the box. Sometimes rugs have to be removed, only paper being permitted.

One final word on travel generally. If the journey is likely to be a long one with changes it is better for the bitch to travel overnight. The dog, having been active all day, invariably sleeps through the night journey and arrives much fresher, and conditions are quieter at stations where changes are made and there is less risk of missed connections.

Responsibilities of the Owner of the Bitch

1. *Fixing the date, and mode of despatch for the mating* Having decided on the stud dog to be used, the owner of the stud dog should be given early notification of the proposed date of mating; hence the importance of the first sign of showing colour, the date of the service being fixed from this day. Usually this is eleven days afterwards, unless the best mating time for a particular bitch is known. If the stud dog owner is careful not to over-use his dog he may refuse to accept a bitch at short notice; his dog may have served at too short an interval beforehand. Therefore the service should be booked well in advance. The next point to decide is whether to take the bitch to the dog or despatch her by rail. Distance and circumstances govern this, but whenever the bitch can be taken by the owner it is more satisfactory to do so. The bitch is less nervous, the owner can see the actual mating and assist if the stud dog owner wishes it. Further, the business side of the transaction can be completed on the spot. As it is impossible to predict how long the mating will take it is inadvisable for the owner to have other engagements that day. When it is impossible to accompany the bitch the stud dog owner should be given definite instructions and information regarding the train journey, notifying him of the time of departure and time of arrival in order that the bitch can be met without any delay. A 'phone message or wire on the actual day, confirming despatch, is useful.

2. *The travelling box* A strong travelling box should be used. British Railways' rules are that it must be big enough for the dog to stand up and turn round in, this applying to any size breed. It should have good ventilation holes, but it is preferable for the box to be enclosed so that the bitch cannot see out, this being less disturbing to her when waiting on a crowded platform. It must be well secured, but whatever locking device is used it must be such that it can be opened in an emergency during transit and by the stud dog owner on arrival. Methods involving nuts and bolts which can be lost are undesirable, as also are split pins.

Quite the simplest method, giving completely adequate security, is the following: the door or lid has an ordinary gate latch or loop which fits over a staple or ring which is *fixed* to the box. The scissors-grip catch end of a dog lead, with about three inches of the leather, is fixed to the box at a distance that will allow the grip to engage the ring when the loop is over it. Thus *all* parts are fixed to the box and none can be lost, and attaching the lead catch to the ring staple is a matter of a second only. The bitch's own rug or blanket (of which she knows the smell) should be placed inside; alternatively, some clean straw or wood-wool. A collar and lead should accompany the box but not be worn. A bitch rarely wants to eat when travelling, but a handful of small biscuits should be included in case she does on a long journey.

3. *Labels* Advice on labels is the same as that given in the previous section (5), dealing with the return of the bitch by the stud dog owner.

4. *Condition of the bitch* It should be a matter of personal pride on the part of the owner that the bitch is sent in the best possible condition. For her nuptials she should be brushed, groomed, bathed, shampooed, or whatever is the customary method for the bitch to be turned out in an immaculate condition. It is the height of bad form, and most inconsiderate to the owner of the dog, to send a bitch who is dirty, her hind parts unwashed, and her hair there matted. In the case of long-haired, heavy-coated breeds, it is usual to cut away all the hair in the vicinity of the vulva, the rump and upper parts of the hind legs. This not only tidies up the bitch but assists negotiation by the dog. A mass of hair would act as a buffer and impede penetration. It is usual for this to be done before the bitch is despatched, since the stud dog owner should not do it without permission. If it becomes essential for him to do so he should use his discretion but inform the bitch owner of the necessity for his action. In any case the bitch will be off the show bench for four or five months and the lack of hair will not be detrimental during that time, unless she has show engagements to fulfil during the first four to five weeks of her pregnancy. Thereafter she is usually unshowable and loses her coat at whelping. The cutting away of the hair is also beneficial at actual whelping time. To despatch a verminous bitch is a disgrace; to send one infected with, or who has been in contact with, any of the infectious diseases such as distemper or parvovirus is a crime. Always make sure that both animals are fully inoculated at the time of service. If in doubt consult your veterinary surgeon regarding a booster. Imagine your own chagrin if you had your valuable Kennel of show and breeding stock wiped out as a result of accepting an infected or in-contact bitch. Stud dog owners are quite within their rights to refuse to mate a bitch in unclean or verminous condition, and are justified in immediately returning it to the box and putting it on the next train back.

Such cases have occurred and will occur. As a bitch owner, guard your reputation; if the bitch is worth mating she is worth grooming. However keen you are for a litter, and whatever the loss would be, sacrifice your own ends rather than risk loss to another breeder by sending him an infected bitch.

5. *Number of matings* Some bitch owners request or insist that two services be given within an interval of two days; in such cases the owner of the dog must comply. If, however, a first service was satisfactory in every way, and both animals are potent and fertile, a second service is of questionable value; however, some breeders like to have it as a 'belt and braces' provision. If there is the slightest doubt about the adequacy of the service an interval of a day or two can elapse and a second service then be given, when the bitch may be more ready and other conditions causing the doubt be more propitious. Again, if a bitch is undergoing a course of hormone treatment for fertility, or increased prospects of conception, under a veterinary surgeon he usually specifies days and times when matings shall be done, and sometimes requires the bitch to be mated three times—once very early, a second at the average time, a third very late. The bitch owner should give details of the services required, with particular instructions in the case of a bitch under treatment. With these the stud dog owner should comply.

6. *Return* It is courteous for the bitch owner to notify the stud dog owner, by 'phone or wire, of the safe return of a bitch.

Use of open-ended feeder – the puppy must be
held upright

Use of the Belcroy feeder – do not pinch the rubber teat
if the puppy is sucking satisfactorily

Opposite and above: Application of a tape muzzle – if muzzling becomes
necessary, always use soft material

A drop in temperature is often an indication
of imminent whelping

Newspaper makes good bedding material – note whelping
box and rail

Post parturient Afghan in typical protective 'U' shape.
Later she will relax more

Chapter 3

Idiosyncrasies in the behaviour of a dog or bitch at mating time—Stud dog behaviour—Reactions of the bitch—When necessary to muzzle the bitch; procedure.

The Dog

The behaviour, mannerisms and peculiarities of dogs at mating time are very variable, therefore the novice must accept at the outset that hard-and-fast rules for management cannot be laid down. He must appreciate that he must learn by observation the individual mannerisms of his own dog or dogs, and into which class each can be placed. One rule that can be laid down, however, is that whatever idiosyncrasy a dog shows at its *first* service, so will it *always* behave, and must always be allowed to behave thus and be treated accordingly. It can be regarded as belonging to a certain type. From general experience it is considered that a dog seldom changes its original technique. Once a dog's method has been determined it is easy to know how to manage him.

Types

To classify stud dogs into types one would say there are four:

1. *The aggressive, cave-man type* This dog knows exactly what the bitch has come for and wastes no time on preliminaries. He will mount immediately, and if the bitch is at the optimum period of readiness and is co-operative he will negotiate easily. Penetration is effected in a flash—like a trout up stream. Provided the dog is not too aggressive, lucky is his owner as many difficulties are removed. With this type, however, one must be careful with a highly strung, nervous, non-cooperative bitch. The dog must be restrained a little; holding him on a lead, induce him to be more gentle and at least give the bitch time to appreciate the situation and become amenable. If this type is allowed immediately to serve a nervous bitch she tends to become still more frightened. Her muscles tighten instead of relaxing, making penetration

41

by the dog much more difficult. She will snap, or actually bite, doing all she can to avoid the union by turning and pulling herself away or rolling on the ground. Gently restraining the dog, and patiently soothing the bitch, will in the end bring about the desired result, but assistance must not be hurried; great patience is required.

2. *The average type* of dog is neither too premature and aggressive nor too sluggish and unintelligent. Instincts may develop slowly; he will want to take his time, and will sometimes move away, sit down and think it all over, then come back to the bitch with renewed eagerness. He usually wants to demonstrate his affection by nuzzling his head against her and licking her ears. He is in no way put off by the coquettishness of a ready bitch, who will run around, then stand, and then run about again; he plays up to it and prefers this preliminary flirtation to the downrightness of the 'cave-man'. This type is eminently suited to the natural or love mating and, provided the assistant does not try to hurry either dog or bitch, this can be regarded as the normal, straightforward, simple service. In ordinary circumstances, we strongly advise the love mating, and the more natural the service can be kept the better. It is only when idiosyncrasies occur, and difficulties arise with either dog or bitch, that its practice should be departed from. But it calls for time and patience on the owner's part. He must give the lovers opportunity to decide for themselves when they wish to make the union complete, and only then intervene in certain ways to assist the mating. The methods of assistance are discussed in the next chapter. Again, the owner who possesses this average type dog is fortunate; although a bit slow, his dog makes a sure and sound stud dog and gives very little real difficulty.

3. *The jittery type* Some dogs are nervous, shy, difficult, timid and fussy; they appear to be overawed by the proceedings. If the bitch becomes skittish and chases such a one he will run away, not in the playful mood she is exhibiting but from stage fright at her unseemly advances. When a degree of excitement has been created he will diffidently mount, but drops away again. He peers apprehensively at the bitch, and is put off by the slightest discouragement. He is the complete opposite of the 'cave-man'. Even when mounted and doing his utmost to serve her, if the bitch is snappy and is allowed to turn her head, show her teeth or growl (as some bitches do) his ardour is completely quenched; he drops away and sometimes won't play again. When this type, after exhibiting all the jitters mentioned above, does eventually penetrate he must at once be pushed firmly up to the bitch and kept there, otherwise his fussiness will cause him to slip out again as soon as he has negotiated. Further, even when tied and functioning he continues to jitter, is restless, and when turned will pither about on

all four feet. He tries to come apart or wriggle, which causes an occasional cry of pain from the bitch. With this type there is unquestionably a need for two assistants. A single-handed mating here can be very distracting and irritating, but with two persons it can be entirely simplified. One would regard this as the most difficult type of stud dog, but if he is by conformation and points a grand specimen and throws good progeny it is obvious that he must be persevered with, humoured, and gradually trained.

They may improve a little but they never completely shed their diffidence. They will never become he-men. If your stud dog is of this type you must fervently hope that all bitches coming to him will be docile, ready and co-operative. If they are not, the difficulties are accentuated. But difficulties are made to be overcome and these can be countered. Have two persons present. However coquettish the bitch may be, this type of dog never responds to the natural mating. Therefore don't waste time by expecting him to react normally and do not give the bitch an opportunity to flaunt her bold wares before him. She should at once be held stationary, facing straight to the front, by one assistant placing a hand on each side of her head and neck, grasping her reasonably firmly so that she cannot turn round or even move from this position. That is one assistant's job throughout the whole proceedings—to keep the bitch still and prevent her turning her head. If she is ready and co-operative and curling her tail the dog will in due course attempt a tentative mounting; let him do this a few times as stimulation usually increases with each. The other assistant should be on the alert to watch for the first actual negotiation, and then immediately press the dog closely to the bitch and very fimly hold him there.

With this type it is very inadvisable to attempt to turn the dog too soon; often it is better not to do so at all. Hold him in close contact with the bitch throughout and let him jitter and dither there; it makes for a more certain conception with less risk of hurting the bitch. It is tiring for the assistant, but necessary. If the dog is too diffident even to mount and attempt penetration himself, he is the type which requires the guided or forceful method, described later. The attitude of this type is not due to lack of sexual instinct, which may be quite keen, but to lack of confidence and marked shyness.

4. *The sluggard* In all breeds some young dogs are sluggish, lethargic and quite unintelligent as far as the service is concerned. They are sexual nitwits. They are similar to the shy and nervous type, the only difference being that in the former the sexual instinct is normal, while with the sluggard it is underdeveloped or lacking. This is the only type where changes in behaviour do ultimately occur; as the dogs get older, and

with each service accomplished they show improvement. They are the most difficult type to deal with, but fortunately they are only a very small minority.

It is necessary for the assistant to resort to hand stimulation by rubbing the penis and, if response results to the erectile tissue, guiding the penis to the vulva and actually inserting it, which is the forcible mating. In time this practice educates the dog sexually and it will gradually become less necessary to employ it. One has experience of such a dog eventually becoming quite a sound and average stud dog, but his first half-dozen or so services called for a lot of patience. If the first is at about ten months, and such a dog appears to be quite impotent after trying all our resources, it is better to postpone further attempts for about three months, and hope that further development will reduce the sluggish tendency.

Hand friction is sometimes required to a slight extent with types 2 and 3 also, if they appear to be uninterested. In many cases it has the desired effect but some dogs resent it completely, and it has the opposite effect, putting the dog off entirely. This is an example of the necessity of knowing the dispositions of each of one's individual stud dogs. Another example: although it has been mentioned that sometimes it is necessary to assist a dog by pressing him to the bitch, some dogs will be put right off if touched at all. Two further general remarks concerning classes 2, 3 and 4 are, first, that the dog should be encouraged by using his name in a praising tone—he should know that he is acting with your approval. (This because they have sometimes been scolded for acting on a natural impulse on occasions when quite definitely they should not.) Never be harsh with a young, untrained stud dog during a service; to be impatient defeats your object. The second suggestion may sound rather too simple to mention. If a dog is being very dilatory, and not getting on with the job, pretend to take the bitch away by lifting her up, if a small breed, or leading her out of the room if a large breed. At the same time use such phrases as, 'We'll take her away', or, 'We'll send her back.' When there are several stud dogs available (they invariably know what is afoot and usually some jealousy is apparent), and the selected one appears uninterested in the bitch, say, 'Oh, we'll use Bob instead and take Bill back,' and pretend to lead Bill off. The use of such threats and actions always increases excitement to a surprising extent, and it will be found when the bitch is put on the floor, or brought back again, the dog will mount at once and negotiate quickly. Such simple advice may appear almost childish, but anyone with experience amongst dogs will agree that they do uncannily understand.

The Bitch

Compared with the dog, mannerisms in the bitch are considerably fewer, making any classification into types unnecessary. Provided one has been able to time the service with the period when the bitch is at her most ready stage and curling her tail, practically all will stand quite willingly and passively to be mated. The majority of bitches are of this type. It is possible that at the time of actual union bitches have a much keener sexual instinct than young dogs under instruction. Bitches very seldom exhibit their sexual instinct at any time other than at the oestrum, while dogs evince it frequently at other times but appear to be less keen than the bitch at the actual time.

Some maiden bitches are very scared, partly due to strangers and strange surroundings, partly due to fear and the roughness of a dog. A few are inherently snappy and even vicious. A bitch is always more docile and less scared or anxious at her second and subsequent matings. On introducing a maiden bitch to the stud dog you should quickly decide how she is going to react. If she is coquettish and plays at once you can expect her to behave like the majority of bitches, and the service will be simple and straightforward. If she instantly runs away, trying to hide behind something, or stands at bay, snarls or shows her teeth to the dog, this is due to fear or distaste for this particular dog, which is not overcome by leaving the dog and the bitch together in the hope that they will mate naturally. Further, if the stud dog is young and inexperienced he can be completely put off stud work for some time if the bitch continually snaps and growls at him, and an otherwise promising stud dog's future is marred.

When bitches are perhaps a day previous to their best ready stage, or perhaps a day past it, they are still perfectly mateable. Generally they are more willing and co-operative after than before. In such circumstances the bitch will frequently not be responsive and co-operative but will snap and show resentment to the dog. In this case, as with the frightened maiden bitch, the manner of handling them is the same. They should be addressed in a soothing tone, very gently and coaxingly, using their own names but at the same time be firmly made to stand, and be held in position.

It is with the snappy or frightened type of bitch that muzzling is strongly advocated. The following method is recommended as it is simple, rapid and perfectly effective.

Having handy as already mentioned a length of 1½-inch wide bandage or alternatively the leg of a pair of tights or an old tie, make a single loop in the middle, holding the ends. Slip this over the muzzle and pull tightly to ensure that the jaws are not capable of opening. Bring the ends down under the muzzle and tie with one throw, then take the ends back behind the head and tie in a bow over the neck. It is amazing how rapidly this can be done, and how this seems at once to quieten a fractious bitch. Securing the ends over her neck restrains her from turning her head and considerably restricts any movement of the head at all. In necessary cases, probably quite infrequent, it is a complete protection for owner and dog from being bitten by a frightened or vicious bitch, and at the same time the bitch becomes more tractable. Other antics of a not quite ready bitch are attempting to sit or lie down, or a determined effort to roll on her back.

It is with this occasional difficult bitch behaviour that it is most advisable for there to be two people to assist at the mating.

Both dogs and bitches can be quickly put off, sometimes at a crucial moment, by an unexpected noise, a sharp voice, too much loud conversation between assistants, particularly if one or both are strangers. Consequently, when possible a quiet and secluded room or site should be chosen for the mating, where the barking of other dogs will not be heard. Conversation should be reduced to a minimum and be carried on quietly. The door should be locked to prevent intrusions; this is mentioned because one has had experience of dogs dismounting at preliminary stages because the door has been unexpectedly and noisily opened.

An attempt has been made in this chapter to cover all contingencies a novice may meet in the behaviour of dogs or bitches at mating time. Stress is again laid on the fact that most services are simple, straightforward and trouble-free and form an interesting part of the dog-breeding hobby. The information should not confuse or deter the novice but, rather, place him in a position to cope with a difficulty as it arises. He should not now be caught unawares by unexpected behaviour of either dog or bitch. To be forewarned is to be forearmed.

Chapter 4

In the last chapter the reactions of dog and bitch at mating time were considered. In this chapter will be described various methods employed to effect the service. The variations in methods are due to the idiosyncrasies already mentioned; they are also necessitated by the varying sizes in a range of over one hundred and thirty breeds. The author has not confined himself to breeds of which he has had practical experience but has sought information from experts in breeds which by size and type could be grouped. It is hoped that guidance will in consequence be found available for the novice whatever the breed of his choice. Each experienced breeder has at some time evolved methods which suit his own ideas, his circumstances and environment, the characteristics and temperaments of his breed or breeds, and by which he has found he gets the most satisfactory results. In the same way the novice will gradually accustom himself to the method which best suits his requirements. Obviously no single method can be advised as the only right way to manage a service.

The Natural Mating

When a stud dog is intelligent, and of the normal average type, and the bitch is ready, willing and responsive, they should be left together for Nature to take her course in whatever manner the pair prefer. By this method there is minimum interference, the assistant standing on one side and taking no part until penetration is on the point of being, or has been, made. Then it is advisable to steady the bitch by holding her head and shoulders facing square to the front. Up to this stage, some breeders go out of the room and watch proceedings through a window, finding that the animals will more readily react if left alone. They return to the room when negotiation is imminent. The only other assistance required is given when one is quite certain the tie has been made (ascertained by feeling under the bitch and noting that the swelling has taken place inside); then the dog can be turned. No attempt should ever be made to turn the dog if the swelling has taken place outside. This can be regarded as the simplest and most normal service, no other interference being necessary than that described. It is the opinion of all breeders that in no circumstances should a dog and bitch be left completely unattended, as has been done by amateurs feeling that such a natural event could be left entirely to the participants. There is a risk of injury to both dog and bitch if this course is followed.

Reference to turning the dog has now been made twice, but the actual operation has not yet been described. When the tie is definite, and there is no risk of separation, the dog's front feet (usually clasped round the bitch if he has not dismounted) are gently placed on the ground on the right side of the bitch, the two then facing the same direction and standing side by side. The dog's left hind leg is then gently raised and carried over the bitch's back to the right side while the dog himself turns in the direction in which the bitch's rear is facing. The left foot is then placed on the ground, while the right one has moved towards the left side. Thus the left foot now stands where the right did, and the right foot where the left did, with the feet pointing in the completely opposite direction. It is a sound plan to grasp both animals' tails and hold them firmly together in one hand, if they are of sufficient length; this prevents any attempt at dragging away until the right time. It is astonishing how both dog and bitch seem to prefer this turned position, remaining steady and passive.

The Assisted Mating, Single-handed

We will now consider a situation in which a stud manager receives a bitch for mating, has no one available to assist and must supervise the service on his own. There are two possible methods, detailed in order of preference. They are most suitable for the smaller breeds up to Fox Terrier size and particularly so for the short-legged breeds, such as Corgis, Dandie Dinmonts, Scotties, Cairns, West Highlands, Dachshunds, Sealyhams, etc.

(a) *On the Floor* The manager can use a hassock, a low stool, a bale of straw, or a rolled mat, on which he himself sits, about six to twelve inches above the ground, with his legs wide apart and knees slightly raised. He places the bitch across his left leg below the knee, and nearer to or farther from the knee according to the height of the breed. The bitch's belly is thus supported by the leg; the height of the vulva can be raised to the dog by drawing up the knee, or can be lowered by dropping the leg and stretching the bitch's hind legs outwards. The dog is brought inside the right leg and either himself mounts or is placed in the mounting position. Mating is then allowed to take place. The advantages of this method are that the manager, while gaining a large measure of control over the bitch's position with his left leg, has both hands free. Thus, whether the bitch has been fractious and was muzzled, or had only a collar and lead on, the manager can with his left hand easily hold the lead or muzzle, or support the neck and shoulders. The main object of this procedure is to keep the bitch's head facing front and prevent her turning round. At the same time the right hand is free to give the dog any assistance that may be required, and to keep him pressed close to the bitch to prevent slipping out in the early stages.

In the case of the large breeds and the long-legged dogs, such as Setters, Mastiffs, Danes, Borzois or Irish Wolfhounds, it is obvious that this method would not be practicable. I have learned that it is extremely rare among the big breeds for anyone to attempt to control a service single-handed, that as the breeds get bigger the breeders always try to have a second person present. When a single-handed service with a big breed is unavoidable the manager should stand up, and raise one knee with his foot resting on a stool, thus supporting the bitch's belly over the knee.

(*b*) *The Table Method* There are many breeders among the smaller and low-to-ground breeds who prefer to work on a table rather than on the floor. In such cases it is still advocated that with a co-operative pair the preliminaries of the natural mating should be allowed on the floor, and the animals not placed on a table until stimulation has occurred for both, as a result of some acquantance. It is obvious that any form of table method is quite unsuitable for most of the big breeds.

The Hitching-Post Method

As an adjunct to the table method there is the hitching-post method. This consists of securing to one end of the table a piece of wood, slightly higher than the shoulder height of the dogs, and fixing into this a strong staple at shoulder height. Alternatively, the table can be placed firmly against a wall and the staple fixed at the right height into the wall. By tying the bitch's lead close to the staple, allowing only about six inches of lead from collar to staple, another effective means of controlling the bitch's head and preventing her turning round is gained. This method leaves the hands free when one has to supervise a mating by oneself, when both hands are required to manipulate the vulva and the penis, and adjust the one to the other. Generally the bitch stands quite passively when controlled on a tight lead in this way, and it is impossible for her to snap at, bite or in any way put off a raw young stud dog under service training.

In single-handed matings among the big breeds a staple in a wall at the shoulder height of the dog when standing on the floor is the alternative to the table hitching-post method for the small breeds. The bitch is secured by it close up to the collar, thus giving the manager more freedom of manoeuvre at her rear end when he need pay no further attention to her head end. With the big and long breeds, such as the Deerhound, Wolfhound or Borzois, this advice will be found most helpful.

Choice between the floor method and the table method is often determined by the stud dog himself; some will mate readily on the floor but refuse to do so if placed on a table.

The way in which a dog first serves or is trained to serve will be the way he will always prefer.

The Assisted Mating with Two Assistants

(*a*) *Small and Low-to-ground Breeds* When two people are able to take part in the management of a service it is considerably simplified and can be carried out with greater certainty, efficiency and comfort for the dogs. Mention has already been made of the difficulties which may be met with, and of certain actions by the dog and the bitch which must be prevented. These can be recapitulated thus: (1) A bitch being scared and running away from the dog; (2) A dog being nervous and continually slipping out after penetration; (3) A bitch sitting on the floor or rolling on her back at each attempt of the dog to mount; (4) A bitch snapping at and biting the dog on first introduction; (5) A bitch repeatedly turning her head and straining away when mating is first effected. Any or all of these things can tend to put off a young stud dog and perhaps permanently ruin him for the work. They can all best be avoided by having two persons to assist at the service. Each should have a definite job to do and keep to his own job. Responsibility can be quite simply divided: one attending to the head end of the bitch, the other to the rear end and to the requirements of the dog. Each is of equal importance, and together they can prevent the untoward happenings already mentioned.

With the small and low-to-ground breeds the following is a routine procedure: we will call the assistant at the head end A and the one at the rear end with the dog B. Assuming that the bitch is one of the fractious type, and that muzzling is decided upon, A proceeds to fix the bandage muzzle, while B smears the vulva with Vaseline, and makes a digital exploration for the reasons already given. These preliminaries ended, A can either kneel on a cushion or sit on a low stool, and grasp the bitch's head, neck or shoulders on each side firmly, at the same time speaking to her soothingly. His main purpose is to prevent her from suddenly swinging round. This is most likely to occur at the actual moment of penetration, when the bitch frequently gives a sharp cry or whimper, and it is for this that A must keep an alert watch to anticipate it, and exert firm control just at this stage. Depending entirely on what may be expected in the temperament of a bitch, A's job may be simply the quiet one of a lightly restraining hand on the bitch's neck whilst caressing her with the other, if she has a normally tranquil temperament. Or the job may become something of a wrestling match if she is of the supersensitive type, highly strung, scared and vicious, and in such cases he does his job correctly only if he has held the bitch so firmly that she has been unable to swerve round suddenly, causing the dog to slip away, or in any other way interfere with him or put him off the performance of his natural function. If the bitch does not calm down however, the service should be aborted, the 'contestants' separated and consideration be given to using another dog or trying again later.

According to the size of the breed, B can either assume the same sitting position as in the single-handed mating, having full use of both hands, or he can kneel on a cushion or sit on a low chair. B's main jobs are, firstly, to decide whether the bitch is standing too low or too high for the dog, and adjusting the bitch to him by raising or lowering the vulva with the finger of the left hand. If the bitch is too high her hind legs should be stretched well apart and the dog given a folded rug to raise his hind feet. If the bitch is too low, she should be given the folded rug for her hind feet to rest on. Secondly, having thus assisted negotiation B should be ready at the moment of penetration to press the dog's rump firmly to the bitch as this can be regarded as the most critical phase, because of the tendency of the bitch to swerve and of the dog to slip out. Instantly the dog will himself start working and if his idiosyncrasies will permit we prefer to maintain the pressure by B during the dog's exertions, relaxing it only when the dog's efforts are over and it can be determined that the swelling has taken place inside and a tie effected. Thirdly, B is in the best position to turn the dog when the time comes.

(*b*) *The Large and Tall Breeds* As one moves up the scale of breeds taller than Fox Terrier size, and longer than Dachshunds and Dandies, modifications of method will become necessary for the two assistants at the assisted mating of the bigger and longer breeds up to the Danes and Wolfhounds. For the intermediate sizes the following are suggested methods:

(1) A stool or low chair is placed on the floor beside the bitch. B places his left foot on this, raising his bent knee until it supports the bitch's belly. A concentrates only on the bitch's head and shoulders, as with smaller breeds. Thereafter all the previously described general principles are observed. With an obstinate bitch disposed to sit, lie or roll, both A and B, standing on opposite sides of the bitch, place a foot on the stool or chair alongside each other and with the sides of their knees in close contact can make a bridge under the bitch. Each has two hands free to attend to his department. This method of encirclement gives a good measure of control as, in addition to pressure of the assistants' bodies against the sides of the bitch, she can be adroitly manoeuvred from underneath. It is helpful with the heavy breeds, such as Bull-Mastiffs and Danes.

(2) A further modification for the biggest and heaviest breeds is for A and B to stand opposite each other with the bitch between them, A a little nearer the head end and B the rear end. A places his left hand under the bitch and B's left hand is likewise placed there, each grasping firmly the other's wrist. Here again a useful controlling and encircling bridge is made. Control here is even better than with the knees, but each has only one free hand, either for A to keep the bitch's head straight or for B to maintain pressure against the dog's rump.

The Guided or Forcible Mating

In addition to the methods and modifications already mentioned there is a school of breeders who adopt tactics greatly differing from any so far described. This can be termed the guided or forcible mating and its principles can be made applicable either to the table method or the floor method, and it is undertaken either singlehanded or by two persons.

As before, when the animals are co-operative the natural love-play preliminaries should be indulged in for a little time. Breeders who practise the guided mating find that they get more satisfactory results by not giving the dog an opportunity to try to effect the mating himself, and at once assist him to negotiate and penetrate. The following is a description of this method. The passage having been examined by a sterilized and lubricated finger, and the pair having become acquainted, and the dog appears ready to serve, an assistant A lifts the bitch on to a table of good length but not too wide (approximately 4 feet long by 2 feet wide). A holds the bitch by grasping with each hand the loose skin on each side of the neck. If A presses his elbows to his sides, making the forearms rigid, the bitch is kept steady without exerting undue pressure on the neck. B then places the dog on the table, passing his left forearm underneath the bitch, with the flat hand, palm upwards, protruding on the far side. This prevents the bitch sitting when the dog mounts. The dog then mounts and B with his right hand carefully guides the dog's penis to the bitch's vulva, and actually inserts it. Insertion and penetration having been effected, B now immediately removes his right hand and places it, fingers downwards, flat against the dog's rump with the thumb round the base of the tail. B then gives him a gentle lift with the right hand and the dog places his hind feet on B's left hand and forearm, so obtaining a platform. By gripping the base of the tail the dog can be controlled if he is too vigorous. In due course, and conditions being propitious, the dog is turned in the usual way, both tails being grasped together in one hand.

Clearly this method cannot be employed with all breeds; it is one suitable mainly for the small and the short-legged varieties. It is favoured by terrier breeders of the Cairn, Scottie and Sealyham types.

The *principle* of the guided mating may be followed with any breed, with or without a table. Compromise and modifications become necessary as breeds increase in size and where the use of a table would be impossible. With the larger breeds, when single-handed a combination of the hitching-post (staple in wall) and the guided mating is a satisfactory and popular method.

The guided method has much to recommend it. Its devotees claim that much time is saved, and much useless expenditure of energy on the dog's part avoided. In the other methods it cannot be denied that dogs do fumble and jitter for a considerable time, until they make contact with the penis against the vulva. When contact is made, however, penetration is usually instantaneous. It is finding the vulva which seems to be the dog's biggest difficulty; when found for him by the last method described the dog is quick to appreciate the contact and reacts rapidly. Fruitless efforts to find the vulva tend to make dogs impatient and erratic, and they will sometimes spend themselves outside the bitch as a result. The chief advantage of the method, then, is the saving of time and avoidance of waste of energy by the dog. The chief disadvantage is that many dogs resent being handled at all, and are completely put off if touched.

The opening remarks in this chapter showed that there is no one and only correct method of managing a service. But the novice, and perhaps more experienced breeders, should now be in a position to overcome any difficulty encountered with any breed. If one method fails, the novice now has knowledge of alternatives. After a few cases, with fresh practical experience gained at each, he will be able to arrive at a routine suiting his individual requirements and the requirements of the breed of his choice, and more particularly the peculiarities of his own dogs.

Chapter 5

Again the reader can have a respite from the intricate details of stud work in so far as they concern actual mating.

Stud work is a business and there is much to be learnt regarding its financial side, as will be explained in this chapter. Many difficulties can arise with the business side of a stud. The following guidance may help the novice and prevent embarrassment. There are certain unwritten laws which have come to be recognized as accepted customs and usages. When obeyed they help to bring to a satisfactory conclusion any contract entered into; when departed from, bad feeling is created, muddles and mistakes in pedigrees occur, and in extreme cases litigation has to be resorted to, or censure from the Kennel Club is invoked.

The Stud Fee

This is entirely a matter for the stud dog owner to fix. The amount is extremely variable, being dependent on the popularity of a breed, supply and demand in that breed, the achievements and qualifications of the dog and, finally, the quality of the progeny the dog throws. With some breeds the fee is as low as £25; in some cases a stud fee of £250 has been charged.

Taking a general average of all breeds, the fee for a top-ranking dog, the quality of whose progeny is known to be equal to that of his own, would be over £100. For good specimens, either champions or big prize winners, the average is around £150. For lesser lights and dogs used perhaps only for pet litters, the average fee is £25–40. It is advisable for a novice with a good dog not to overcharge for its early services, or until its progeny has been proved; bitch owners are chary of using an unknown dog and in these days of financial stringency the dog might get no work if a large fee were asked. It is better gradually to increase the fee as the dog's potentialities warrant, and quite legitimate to increase it when the progeny is proved to be prize-winning stock, and the dog himself enhances his qualifications. As a simple example, if a really good dog in an average breed begins at £25 it would be sound to charge about £50–60 after each of the first two CCs are gained. On becoming a champion this can be increased up to £200, and with some stud dogs with multiple CCs more than this. If the progeny was proving excellent from a variety of bitches, showing that the dog was prepotent, which means capable of *always* producing his own qualities from a large range of bitches, for this reason alone an increase up to £50–75 is justifiable. If the dog becomes a multiple CC winner, and his services are much in demand, and the owner does not wish him to be overworked or abused, it is fair and advisable to limit the number of bitches served while at the same time maintaining his own deserved financial reward by increasing the fee to between £200 to £250.

Approved Bitches

It will be appropriate here to explain this term. It is a common fallacy among newcomers to imagine that it is always the stud dog who is responsible for the excellence of the progeny, and to think that because a dog is a marvellous champion embryo champions will always be sired by him out of inferior bitches. This is far from the truth. It is an established fact that some super-excellent dogs never sired a worthwhile specimen in the whole course of their careers, which confirms that the real value of a stud dog lies in the quality of his progeny, not in the excellence of the dog himself. The bitch plays just as great, perhaps a greater, part in determining the number of the progeny and particularly the quality. This fact is the basis of another breeding dictum—that only specimens of the highest quality should be selected for mating if equally high quality is to be expected in their offspring. The owner of an exceptionally good dog siring good stock is extremely unwise if he accepts for service all and sundry bitches of a mediocre or even inferior or bad calibre. If he does so it is inevitable that a large number of bad specimens, probably whole litters of nondescript stock, will be let loose, all bearing his dog's name as sire. The average breeder, ignoring the fact that the bitch (dam) is equally or more responsible, is quick to note the inferiority of the stock the stud dog is throwing, and it rapidly becomes published abroad that this quite good sire produces faulty progeny. Then the dog as a stud dog will be dropped like a hot penny. So is a stud dog's reputation damned. But an astute sire owner, with a stud dog of proved achievement and proved as an excellent stock getter out of suitable bitches with line-bred pedigrees, takes care not to have his dog's prospects so ruined. He is far-sighted enough to see that it is better for his Kennel account in the long run to have fewer stud fees rather than let his dog lose reputation. He ensures that bad stock shall never be discussed as having been sired by his dog, by being discriminating in the bitches he accepts for the dog to serve, and advertises the service to approved bitches only. He may want to see the pedigree of the bitch to make sure that the blood lines are compatible with those of his dog, and he will wish to see her to convince himself that her quality is such that only good stock can justifiably be expected. He reserves the right to refuse to accept for service an inferior bitch with glaring faults. Ultimately he is unquestionably a gainer and not a loser; the progeny start to win, and as no bad specimen has been mated by his dog the demand for its services will steadily increase, with an increasing stud fee, instead of income being cut off short as a result of evidence of bad stock. To go back to beginnings (after visions of magnificent stud fees!), it is quite customary on introduction of a new dog to advertise him without fee for a service or two, to prove him. This is fair, as the dog might be sterile, or impotent, and a fee would have been taken with no prospect of value in return. Until a dog is a proved sire perhaps the fairest to both parties is to take no fee at the time of service, but have a written agreement that the fee shall be paid subsequently if the bitch proves in-whelp. Services without fee for the first few times are also useful opportunities for the dog owner to train the dog with no financial worry if some services are abortive. The bitch owner takes the risk of missing a season but wins in the gamble if a litter results, its inception not having cost anything.

At any stage in a stud dog's career an arrangement is sometimes made whereby instead of paying a fee the owner of the bitch will hand over a whelp in lieu. This is generally to the advantage of the stud dog owner, since the selling value of the whelp is greater than the fee, and he has borne no cost of rearing. It is assumed that bitch owners ask for this concession only for personal reasons, in that they do not wish to part with cash. It cannot be too strongly emphasized that any such arrangement should be drawn up in writing, in duplicate to be signed by both parties and one copy retained by each. Gentlemen's agreements either between friends or strangers are well intentioned, but sometimes memories are short. Written evidence is always confirmatory, and in the case of disagreement or non-compliance the written word is proof of the original intention. The document should cover all likely contingencies, so that there will later be no loophole for acrimonious argument. For example, in the case of a puppy in lieu of a service fee, agreement should be arrived at to cover the possibility of only one puppy being in the litter. Strictly, this should go to the stud dog owner; a small litter is an act of fate and bad luck for the bitch owner, but the stud dog owner cannot live on sentiment and must be paid for the service in cash or in kind. Again, if there are two or more puppies agreement should previously have been reached as to whom the first choice goes. If no litter results the stud dog owner has still to be paid for the service, but this is usually avoided by arranging that the same agreement shall be entered into at the bitch's next season. If the bitch whelps a litter the stud dog owner has fulfilled his part, but if all the whelps should die before the stud dog owner receives his pup the bitch owner has not fulfilled his. Here it should have been previously agreed that if for any reason no whelp is forthcoming in lieu of the fee either the fee or part of it shall subsequently be paid to the stud dog owner. Alternatively, the same conditions can be again imposed on the bitch owner, and a puppy shall be due from the subsequent season and litter. The above are only examples of things that should be guarded against. The suggested forms of agreement are not hard and fast rules; the actual terms are for the parties concerned to work out for themselves, but they MUST be previously agreed upon. Generally, a stud dog owner gains a good reputation, and increases his clients, if he tempers hard business instinct with flexibility towards the bitch owner. Whatever the conditions, when once amicably decided upon they must be put in writing, and thereafter be rigidly observed. Written obligations ultimately fulfilled breed goodwill; haphazard oral agreement may cause ill will.

For What is the Stud Fee Payable?

On this point there is often among novices confusion leading to controversy, since some are under the impression that if no litter results no fee is payable, or that it should be returned. There is no doubt on this point whatever. If the dog is a proved and potent sire the fee is due, being payable for the service itself irrespective of the result. This is a hard and fast unwritten law. Moreover, the stud fee is due in advance before the mating. A stud dog owner having received a bitch by rail would be quite within his rights to refuse to carry out the service until paid. A stud dog owner is selling a service which, like any other commodity, has to be paid for in advance if ordered by mail, or paid for at the time if sold over the counter. One does not expect to buy something in a shop and not pay for it; similarly, stud dog owners cannot afford to run the risk of having to run prolonged credit accounts for stud work. It is unlikely that a stud dog owner would in actual fact stand on this right and leave a bitch to miss a season, but bitch owners should not place the stud dog owner in the position of having to contemplate such a course. However, if a stud dog owner has previously been bilked by an unprincipled bitch owner such experiences might harden him. It is obvious that once a bitch has been served, the goods have been sold; it is also obvious that they cannot be claimed back, because they have not been paid for. It therefore behoves the bitch owner to conform to custom and forward the stipulated fee before a mating is completed.

It is also customary that the stud dog owner shall not bear the expense of the bitch's return journey; the return fare should be prepaid and added to the stud fee. The foregoing is the only financial obligation of the bitch owner to the stud dog owner—but the dog owner has several obligations, general and financial, and if his reputation is to be maintained he should invariably observe the following routine:

A. *If the bitch is brought to him:*

(1) He should parade for inspection the selected stud dog as evidence that it is fit and well, and is the dog who is actually going to be used.

(2) Many stud dog owners prefer that the bitch owner (or person accompanying the bitch) shall not be present at the actual mating as strangers may put the dog off. When the mating is effected, and a tie has resulted, the manager should then call the bitch owner in, as proof of a *bona fide* service. At this stage the animals are seldom put off; the bitch owner can remain, and by caressing the bitch increase her comfort and confidence.

(3) If no actual tie has been effected the stud dog owner has to make an honest decision himself by answering these questions: Was this mating adequate? Can a litter reasonably be expected? Am I justified in taking a fee? Remember, though, many bitches and dogs do not tie.

It has been mentioned elsewhere that the tie is not an essential, and that a tie lasting an hour has resulted in no litter while penetration for under a minute has produced a record one. In his very earliest experience of stud work the author was perturbed on this point, considering that a mating of extremely short duration could not result in a litter, and was in a quandary as to whether the fee should be returned. Experience has ended such doubts, but the novice requires some criterion to help him to make a decision. The following is suggested:

(*a*) If the dog has taken a dislike to the bitch (sometimes, though very occasionally, this occurs) and he appears to have no stimulation for her, he may make a perfunctory mounting and then show complete disinclination to serve and take no further interest. In such a case it is daylight robbery to accept a fee.

(*b*) The dog has mounted, appears to have penetrated, but *instantly slips away* and is functioning only outside, and if on further attempts the same thing happens no mating can have been effected and no fee should be accepted.

(*c*) If the dog has only very partially penetrated, and obviously all his exertions are futile and he cannot penetrate to any extent, this may indicate a stricture or obstruction in the vagina or a very narrow passage, or that the bitch has dried up or is completely unready. This again indicates a useless mating; no litter can be reasonably expected and no fee should be taken. In these cases there will not have been any swelling of the bulb outside and without this a true service is extremely unlikely.

(*d*) The dog makes complete penetration, has visibly swollen outside at the same time, and when pressed to the bitch remains there, still swollen, for at least ten to twenty seconds and then comes out. This is a state of affairs quite different from the instantly slipping in and out situation. Here a mating can, and almost always does, result in a litter (provided that the bitch is fertile, though fertility or otherwise of the bitch does not affect the question of a legitimate service) and the owner may have complete confidence in accepting the fee. Without this information, he might have had qualms, feeling that the mating was too short. Thereafter while still in the untied position for any period, whether under a minute or remaining so (while held by the assistant) for ten, twenty or thirty minutes, a litter may be expected.

(4) Where there has been no tie the stud dog owner is unable to show the service as evidence. Having come to a decision about the adequacy or inadequacy of the mating, he should straightforwardly explain the circumstances to the bitch owner and if necessary not accept a fee. If the mating was very short, but in his opinion adequate, he should state that he is satisfied that one was effected and that a litter will result. The fee is then fully justified.

B. If the bitch is sent by rail Except that the stud dog cannot be paraded, or the tie shown, the same procedure is followed, and details of the service should be sent either by 'phone or letter. Occasionally the stud dog owner is unable to effect a mating by the dog selected but considers one might be possible by another dog. He should at once communicate with the bitch owner, requesting permission to use another dog. It would be most unwise to use a different dog without first obtaining this permission.

The service having been satisfactorily effected, the stud dog owner must supply the bitch owner with the dog's pedigree or with its stud card. This enables the bitch owner to make out the pedigree of the whelps in the forthcoming litter. The stud dog owner must also supply a certificate of the mating and a receipt for the service fee. Mutual obligations are then ended.

The Stud Card

When a dog is established at stud the owner will frequently be asked by prospective users for its particulars. The most convenient and time-saving way of providing this information is by having a stud card printed. The best form is one of cardboard, folded down the centre, thus giving four sides. The front side should be headed by the name of the Kennel, and date of its establishment. It is useful to reproduce a photograph of the dog, with the name above it in bold letters. An unfaked photograph is preferable; it should display the dog's natural points, not a photographer's deceptive skill. Under this, the owner's name and address are inserted, together with telephone number and nearest railway station to which bitches can be sent. On the reverse of the outer page, and on the left of the inside of the folder, a true copy of the pedigree is printed, also details of colour or markings, date of birth, its Kennel Club registration number, or Stud Book number. On the right side of the inside space is left for details of the dog's principal achievements and prize-winning record. On the fourth page, or outer half of the card, a description of the dog is given. This may state any points in the standard in which the dog excels, and any particular feature he is known always to transmit. A reference to temperament is advisable. Following this, the conditions of service should be stated, which include the fee, stating that it must be prepaid, plus cost of return carriage of the bitch. It should state here that though all possible care will be taken of visiting bitches they are accepted only at owners' risk. It is advisable to have this in print as it establishes that a condition of the contract is that the dog owner shall not be held responsible for loss or accident.

Finally, the terms relating to a free service in the event of the bitch missing should be stated.

The Stud Receipt and Certificate of Mating

This can be combined on one form, as in the following example, published by *Our Dogs*, Oxford Road, Station Approach, Manchester:

Many commercial printers have similar forms already printed, which only require overprinting with the owner's Kennel name and address.

STUD SERVICE RECEIPT

Date..19........

Bitch ....

Owner ....

....

Stud Dog ....

Date of Service :—

       1st ....

       2nd ....

Due to Whelp ....

Received Stud Fee £   :

       Signature ....

Other arrangements (if any) :

....

Such Kennel stationery adds to a Kennel's reputation for efficiency. The forms should be detachable, leaving a counterfoil on which the owner can insert the details, providing a convenient record of all bitches served by his dog. The following is an example of the counterfoil:

Date .... 19........

Bitch ....

Owner ....

....

Stud Dog ....

Date of Service :—

     1st ....

     2nd ....

Due to Whelp ....

Stud Fee £ ....

Other arrangements (if any) :

....

....

The Free Service

It is the accepted custom, and a gesture of generosity on the stud dog owner's part, to offer a free service if the bitch misses, i.e. proves not to be in whelp. Usually a free service is offered to the bitch at her next season, but a proviso should be made that this is dependent on the dog still being in the owner's possession. Alternatively, a stud dog owner may offer a service from another dog or to any other bitch, in order that at some future date the bitch owner shall receive some value in return for the fee paid. These must be regarded as *ex gratia* gestures on the stud dog owner's part; he has fulfilled his part of the contract if a service has been adequately accomplished and it is not his responsibility if no litter results.

The stud dog owner should ask the owner of the bitch to inform him of the result of the mating. While it is courteous of the bitch owner always to do so it is essential, if the bitch has missed and a free service is claimed, that information of the failure to whelp should be given within seven days after the due date.

Chapter 6

Records of stud work

Haphazard methods in keeping notes or records of services effected by one or several stud dogs in a Kennel can cause chaos in the compilation of pedigrees.

It must be remembered that the word pedigree implies an accurate account of all the forbears of a dog or bitch; it is a genealogical table. One wrong entry or wrong record can destroy the value of a pedigree, possibly introducing a completely new ancestral line. Scientific breeders who base many of their breeding plans on lines decided upon after the study of a pedigree can have their work wrecked and their plans brought to nought by a single wrong entry. For example, a breeder who might want a certain ancestral dog to appear in the pedigree of a dog he was studying and contemplated using, finds the ancestral dog is included and uses the dog. If, however, the inclusion was an erroneous one the breeder would fondly imagine he was getting into the wanted blood, though in actual fact it was absent. To give another example, a breeder might intend to practise a policy of putting a bitch back to its grandfather, a champion dog, and on referring to his bitch's pedigree he finds the grandsire to use. If in fact the champion dog shown was not the actual grandsire, but entered on the pedigree in mistake for another dog, the bitch owner's breeding plan is abortive. The author knows of many cases where circumstances similar to the above have occurred through negligence or lack of method. Unfortunately, in dog breeding, as in any other walk of life or sport, there is a very small minority by whom shady methods are practised. There have been definite cases of intentionally faked pedigrees, forged in order to give progeny a high value. The Kennel Club has its own regulations for dealing with such cases and the subject is beyond the scope of this book. An attempt will be made, however, to explain to the novice how, by accurate record keeping, he can avoid errors which might involve him in Kennel Club censure.

The Irish Kennel Club has an excellent system for keeping pedigrees accurate. When a dog is registered with them they write to the owner of the stud dog sire, stating that his stud dog is recorded as the sire of the animal to be registered, and requesting verification from the stud dog owner that the mating took place. Our own Kennel Club's present application form for the registration of a dog has undergone many changes of late. Litters of puppies can be registered without actual names and exclusions can be endorsed on registration forms regarding whether or not a dog should be bred from, or exported, etc. In any case, however, the information may be requested months, perhaps years, after the actual mating took place and no breeder can be expected to rely on his memory for an accurate confirmation. A simple recording system removes the strain on memory and ensures efficiency and accuracy. Again, inaccurate records in Show entry forms can cause mistakes and disqualification. A person buys a dog, enters the pedigree details of sire and dam on the entry form, and is ultimately disqualified, the Kennel Club informing him that there is no record of his dog having been sired as stated. It is always advisable to know current registration procedure, which can be obtained from the Kennel Club at 1 Clarges Street, London W1.

The date the service took place is always important; it affects the age of the whelps, which affects their eligibility for entry in certain Show classes.

Many other examples of the penalties of inaccuracy could be quoted, but the foregoing should suffice to make out a case for the necessity of record keeping.

The following are considered to be the essential details of which record should be made:

Each stud dog in a Kennel should have its own page or Record Book headed by his name, his sire and dam, his Kennel Club registration or Stud Book number. The page should be divided into columns, or spaces provided for the following headings:

Column 1. *No. of the service* This is useful in indicating the extent to which a dog has been used, to make comparisons with the other stud dogs, and as a means of quickly ascertaining the financial earnings of the dog.

Column 2. *Date of the service* Important when any query is raised, either by a breeder or by a Kennel Club, requiring verification of a service or pedigree.

Column 3. *Name of bitch served* Essential for verification purposes.

Column 4. *Name and address of owner of the bitch, with telephone number* Necessary if any further correspondence is needed in connection with the service. It is also useful to the owner if he receives frequent offers to buy his stock. If he has no stock of his own available he can either refer the enquiry direct to the bitch owner or undertake to buy in some of the progeny from his own dog, and thus have stock available for resale. Here it is useful to note also the quality of the bitch served, as a guide to whether the progeny would be likely to be up to standard.

Column 5. *Date the bitch is due to whelp* Considered in conjunction with (4), this indicates when progeny from the dog would be available, and also the age of the pups.

Column 6. *Details of the service* These are useful to record as evidence of a possible reason if the bitch proved not to be in whelp. Brief notes should be made on the following points:

(a) The number of days the bitch has been in season.

(b) Whether there was a tie, and its duration.

(c) If no tie the actual time penetration lasted.

(d) Whether the service was straightforward, or whether the bitch was very difficult to serve, being nervous and unco-operative.

(e) Any circumstance which might make conception doubtful.

Column 7. *Result of the mating* Entered when informed by the owner of the bitch of the details of the litter. It should include the total number of whelps, the number of dog pups and number of bitch pups. If it is a breed in which there are many colour variations, the colours of the whelps should be included. These records are useful for the owner subsequently to gauge the potency of his various stud dogs, the proportion of dogs to bitches thrown, and whether a certain dog throws a preponderance of any particular colour.

Column 8. *The date the stud fee was paid and the amount* Useful in assessing the stud earnings of each dog.

Column 9. *Conditions* Finally, space should be provided for a note of the conditions of the service, as for example:

(a) Whether for a fee. (b) Whether for a pup in lieu of the service fee. (c) Any other special condition. (d) If information is subsequently received that the bitch missed it must be recorded that a free service was promised, also of the terms of the free service.

A stud dog owner with many stud dogs serving many bitches in the course of a month will find it difficult to remember exactly the conditions and results of every service, but notes like these will enable him to conduct his stud work accurately and so eliminate any possibility of dispute later.

A final word of advice to the novice stud dog owner; it relates to his advertisements. He may have a very good dog, but the wording of his advertisements perhaps does harm to his prospects because so often it discloses ignorance and inexperience. One can best explain this by examples. One frequently sees a dog advertised as having been 'sired by a bitch' and 'out of a dog' by the wrong use of the words 'ex' and 'by'. The word 'ex' means 'out of' and therefore precedes a dam's name, while the word 'by' precedes a sire's name, indicating that it was sired by that dog. To see a stud dog advertised as 'by' Jane 'ex' Bob, though amusing, destroys confidence. Also, the term 'line-bred' is sometimes inappropriately used. As it implies a breeding–line for many generations it can be applied only to a dog of good age, or even one of a past decade, yet one sees stud dogs described as line-bred to a very recent champion probably only eighteen months old, who could not have had sufficient descendants to make line-breeding from him possible. Further, one perhaps sees a stud dog described as containing the blood of possibly half a dozen leading strains, with names of widely divergent types of champions, quoted by an advertiser presumably under the impression that the greater the number of champions from diverse blood the better the dog must be. To a student of pedigrees this would create a mental picture of an animal resembling a patchwork quilt, rather than of one with a pedigree built up on a scientific plan. Grossly exaggerated advertisements with super-eulogistic phrases cut no ice with the knowledgeable breeder. The novice is therefore advised to stick to true facts correctly stated in moderate language, which are more convincing than flamboyance and palpable inaccuracy.

Part II

Whelping

Preface

SOME of the subject matter of Part II of this book was dealt with in a series of articles in *The Dachshund*, the magazine of the Dachshund Club. The advice given has been acclaimed by novices and experienced breeders alike as being of real value and practical help.

The gist of many letters and expressions of appreciation was that since perusal whelping cases were approached with confidence instead of trepidation.

It was suggested to the writer that the subject should be given greater scope, and that a large number of breeders would benefit if the notes were published in book form and made to cover all breeds. Consequently the articles have been completely revised to make the advice more generally applicable.

It is obvious that with over one hundred and thirty different breeds of dogs there will be whelping factors and eccentricities peculiar to each breed. At the same time, the fundamental, natural biological phenomenon of whelping is constant for all breeds. These general principles of whelping should be known and understood by all owners of bitches of any breed if it is intended that litters are to be bred. Such knowledge will enable them to co-operate intelligently with the veterinary surgeon, particularly when circumstances make the employment of his services essential. Also, the knowledge will help owners to act on their own initiative when difficulties are met with, and when veterinary help is not available. The author has purposely reduced to a minimum theories and technicalities in order that the advice given shall be of a practical nature, based on personal experience over a period of many years. It is confidently prophesied that the lives of many bitches and their whelps will be saved, and much suffering spared them, if this book is studied and its simple, straightforward guidance followed.

It should be remembered that veterinary surgeons are busy people and sometimes irrespective of their wish to do so, it is impossible for their services to be available at the drop of a hat. In consequence, information has been included with a view to saving a bitch from suffering or saving her life and the lives of her puppies when a veterinary surgeon is not able to be present immediately. The veterinary surgeon cannot be expected to stay throughout the whelping, which can

69

sometimes last up to twenty-four hours, and emergencies can arise quickly.

Today the trend is for the veterinary surgeon to ask you to bring the bitch and any puppies into the surgery; this should not be resented since facilities and equipment are then immediately to hand. In addition, the mere act of travelling has been known on innumerable occasions to stimulate the slow starter into action and many a whelp has been born on the back seat of a car proceeding to the vet. On the other hand, even if the veterinary surgeon has arranged to visit, the address may be so sufficiently distant from the practice that unexpected delays can occur—particularly with today's traffic. It is, I hope, in such situations that this book will prove of value, since the knowledge breeders will gain will enable them to act on their own initiative when there is *no* prospect of obtaining professional help. The author knows of definite cases of litters and pups being lost in certain parts of the Commonwealth owing to unavoidable lack of skilled assistance. In many of these fatalities, had the owner practical knowledge and confidence, the tragic losses could have been avoided, a bitch's life saved and a profitable litter reared.

In human childbirth it is by no means rare for delivery to take place before the arrival of the doctor. It is accomplished by the midwife, who has enough knowledge at least to carry on. With a whelping in similar circumstances it is the owner who must turn midwife, and the more knowledge and confidence possessed the better will be the result.

Advice in this book is intended primarily for the newcomer, though procedure with certain of the more advanced cases of abnormality will prove equally instructive to the experienced.

Today there is a vastly increased number of people who have only recently taken up dog breeding as a hobby or a business. Most of these are very enthusiastic, but if one may be permitted to say so, many are woefully ignorant about whelping. This assertion is based on the many SOS 'phone calls one has received at whelping times, and on the innumerable questions asked on the subject.

It is to avoid unnecessary suffering to bitches and their whelps, and disappointments and financial loss to their owners, that it has been decided to put experience into print, in the hope that this may help readers. Care has been taken to ensure that the information given is authentic, that the veterinary aspects are fundamentally accurate, and that no advice given could possibly be harmful.

Descriptions of complications and somewhat lurid details of types of whelping cases are given, to indicate the sort of difficulties that may be met with, so that the inexperienced may know what to expect and thereby avoid being taken by surprise. The advice is based entirely on personal practical experience gained by implicitly carrying out a veterinary surgeon's instructions, and on conclusions formed from whelping cases of several different breeds, but chiefly Dachshunds, over a period of twenty-five years.

Chapter 7

Further reference to practical application of anatomical detail, relating to the bitch only—Principles of whelping—Co-operation with the veterinary surgeon at whelping time

In Part I, The Service, the reason given for describing in detail certain anatomical structures was the value of the practical application of this knowledge. In just the same way anatomical knowledge of the genitals of the bitch will prove beneficial when applied practically in whelping cases.

Figure 2 If assistance is necessary, the whelp should be pulled outwards and downwards at an angle of 45°

(1) *The Vulva* An early sign that actual labour will not long be delayed is that the vulva enlarges considerably, becomes very soft and pliable, which facilitates expansion, and at the same time a clear discharge is observable.

(2) *The Angle of the Vagina* from the vulva. Any breeder may expect to have to assist a bitch to deliver a breech presentation (see relevant chapter and illustrations). It must be emphasized that the pull is in a *downwards* and outwards direction approximately at an angle of 45° to the rump. Any traction in a horizontal direction, or at right angles to the rump, could injure and cause pain to the bitch and whelp, and make the latter's exit more difficult.

(3) *The Length of the Passage* (described in Chapter I, The Service.) The distance from the vulva to the brim of the pelvis or beginning of the body of the uterus; the lumen or width or diameter of the passage; the presence or otherwise of adhesions, are all of the utmost importance. It is explained in a later chapter that it may become imperative to make a digital examination of the passage for the following reasons:

(*a*) In order to find out if a whelp has passed over the brim of the pelvis;

(*b*) to ascertain what complication is causing an obstruction or delay;

(*c*) to determine how far down the passage a whelp actually is;

(*d*) to turn the feet of a breech presentation.

In any such circumstance the anatomical information given in Part I will assist practical manipulation. Here it must once again be stressed that although it is doubtful if any veterinary surgeon would object to a digital exploration of the vagina as a preliminary to a service, the veterinary profession is not keen on amateur interference at whelping since harm and damage to the passage can result unless you know what you are doing. Therefore a novice should not do this until he has gained experience by previously watching the procedure, or does so only in the presence of a veterinary surgeon whom he has asked to instruct him in the matter, in anticipation of an emergency when alone. An experienced breeder can, and often *must*, do so. But in either case the antiseptic precautions mentioned in Chapter I, The Service, must be taken. Again, in either case such digital examination or assistance should be done only when, owing to time lag or other emergency, intervention is necessary and there is no hope of a veterinary surgeon arriving in time, and the owner feels he must do something on his own initiative.

(4) The peculiar arrangement of the uterine horns running along each side of the body indicates during the last two or three weeks of

pregnancy where to make an *external* examination by feeling for the presence and movements of whelps; with experience it is often possible to determine approximately the number of whelps to be expected.

(5) The description of the position of the uterine horns assists, when one *thinks* that the whelping is all over. It is quite impossible for a veterinary surgeon to make an *internal* digital or forceps exploration for a whelp left high up in one of the horns, but by knowing where and how to feel externally the presence of another whelp may be detected when otherwise one might imagine that the bitch had settled down comfortably with her labour trials and tribulations all happily ended. This possibility of an additional whelp, or whelps, is very important, as will be seen from subsequent pages. This is mentioned specifically because so many novices feel for whelps only quite low down in the abdomen, and not much beyond the groin, not realizing the peculiarity of the extensive uterine horns. This knowledge will enable them to ascertain, by external palpation, the presence of whelps when otherwise they would have had no idea where to feel.

Considerable amplification of the above headings will be found in subsequent chapters. They are briefly mentioned here to recapitulate earlier anatomical explanations, and to make more intelligible references to structures.

Further, in the later pages there may crop up odd items of advice which may appear redundant, having already been dealt with in Part I, where it was expedient to discuss them. Many were sub-headings of subjects dealing with breeding generally, and could not be discussed in relation to *either* the service or whelping only.

Principles of Whelping. Co-operation with the Veterinary Surgeon at Whelping Time

No two bitches behave exactly alike at whelping time. It is therefore impossible to lay down hard and fast rules about what may be expected before, during and after the appearance of a litter. Generally speaking, however, the same bitch will behave at each of her whelpings with the same individual mannerisms. These should be noted as they help to determine whether a bitch is a good whelper and good mother or otherwise.

From this broad statement minor exceptions must be made, however. Firstly, although a bitch is a good whelper in her behaviour, and has had two litters with the utmost ease, a complication might arise in her third litter which could result in this whelping being a difficult one.

Secondly, a very excitable bitch at her first litter will often improve at subsequent ones; while a bitch who had great trouble in producing on the first occasion may whelp easily afterwards though still showing her individual mannerisms. A lazy bitch who has no grit and will stand no pain never seems to improve and usually becomes worse and exhibits uterine inertia (described later) to the maximum extent.

A carefully kept record of the details of each whelping will prove invaluable for future reference, and such record-making is strongly advised. Details noted in these records should include:

(1) The number of days before or after the due date that whelping took place.
(2) How many minutes, or hours, elapsed between the arrival of each whelp.
(3) If delivery was normal or required veterinary intervention.
(4) Whether a good or bad whelper, with reasons.

No bitch should be bred from more than twice in three successive heats. Every other season is more humane, reduces the strain on the bitch and may be regarded as ideal. Never hesitate to call in a veterinary surgeon or grudge his fee in the case of whelping. Both your bitch and prospective puppies are valuable, both sentimentally and financially. One puppy saved by the veterinary surgeon more than covers his fee in any case.

Advice must be given about the age when a bitch should be first mated. If a bitch comes into season very early, at from eight to ten months, it is extremely unwise to mate her at this immature age. It is much sounder to wait till the second season, or until the bitch is turned eighteen months of age. The only exception is in the case of miniature breeds, when it is preferable to mate at an early age.

Before a maiden bitch is mated ask your veterinary surgeon to examine her. He may find certain conditions which would make a successful mating impossible, or some abnormality which would endanger the bitch's life at whelping time. Among such conditions are a very narrow vaginal passage, so small as not to allow the passage of the little finger. There may be an obstruction, growth, adhesion or stricture in the passage, which would prevent penetration by the dog. The pelvic bones may be so placed that the passing of even a very small whelp is impossible. In such a case if the bitch becomes pregnant a Caesarian section may be indicated. With modern anaesthesia and equipment this is almost a routine procedure and a few hours after it the bitch may be happily suckling her litter.

Always follow the veterinary surgeon's advice regarding future pregnancies; in some cases he may advise against mating the bitch again. Generally he will find nothing amiss and the mating may be carried out with the satisfaction of knowing that in all probability the whelping will be normal. Had you not arranged this examination your bitch might have had some unsuspected serious abnormality, which would have endangered her life had she been mated and allowed to whelp.

The bitch's normal gestation period is sixty-three days but anything from fifty-eight to seventy-two days can be regarded as normal, depending on the breed. Remember that the date of whelping is always estimated from the date of the first service.

Experience has shown that, in the majority of cases, bitches will go to full term. There is, however, nothing untoward if whelping occurs one, two or three days previously. If a bitch whelps on or before the fifty-eighth day something has gone wrong and generally the pups are too weak and immature to live. There is nothing one can do about this. Earlier miscarriage is extremely rare. It is usually due to some severe shock or violent accident. Should your bitch have a miscarriage it is imperative that you have her examined afterwards by a veterinary surgeon—this is just as important as his attendance during whelping. There is no cause for alarm if a bitch goes one, two or even three days over her time, but beyond the sixty-sixth day matters may not be quite right; it may be evidence of some abnormality, and a veterinary surgeon's attendance is advisable. Forceps delivery, or Caesarean section may be necessary.

The following authentic case is given as an extreme example. A bitch (not the author's) was allowed to go ten days beyond her due date. The owner had been told by another breeder (presumed to be experienced): 'Don't worry; she will be all right.' Result: death of bitch and whelp. Cause: one whelp only, but an enormous one and impossibly big for a bitch of the breed to evacuate. Consequently, during these protracted ten days the whelp had died *in utero*, general septicaemia automatically supervened, with the fatal result. The onus for this fatality must be put on the owner. The correct procedure after three days' delay was to have sought veterinary advice, which would probably have been for an x-ray to be taken. The condition would then have been obvious; the large whelp, probably then alive, could have been safely removed by Caesarean section, reared and possibly ultimately become a CC winner, while the bitch would have lived to produce subsequent litters.

Single large whelps are quite common in old bitches. This fact should help the owner to know what may be expected with them, and underlines the added precaution to be taken in such cases.

A number of other types of abnormality will cause a bitch not to whelp at full term, or within two days of it. Without attention, many could cause the death of the bitch, but with assistance her life could be saved. The moral: never allow your bitch to go more than three days over time without ascertaining from your veterinary surgeon the cause of the delay.

Money spent on a veterinary post natal examination should never be begrudged; it is money and well spent. A single shot of pituitrin to contract the uterus, a course of antibiotics to prevent infection, can be worth their weight in gold in preventing subsequent problems.

Chapter 8

The phenomena of normal whelping in detail—Signs that whelping is imminent—The course of an uncomplicated whelping

Succeeding chapters deal principally with difficulties, abnormalities, and pathological conditions and complications at whelping time. It is quite impossible to understand these without a thorough knowledge of the fundamental processes of a perfectly simple, straightforward, normal whelping. Moreover, as some later details are a trifle unpleasant it is intended that this chapter shall be devoted only to the pleasant part of our hobby—a normal whelping. It is doubtless the gratifying culmination of breeding plans made a year or two in advance; of the service satisfactorily concluded; of several weeks of care and affection from the time your bitch proved in whelp. It is the time when the bitch and her owner are closer together than at any other, and a time when she trusts and has to rely on you implicitly. By confidence and *knowledge* let this be a happy climax for both. Don't wreck plans and aspirations, or let your bitch down through carelessness and ignorance, should the expected normal prove to be abnormal.

Reactions of the Bitch the Day Before She Whelps

Assuming that the mating has been satisfactory, the bitch is safely in whelp, has been properly exercised and if necessary her diet increased and supplemented. She should be examined by your veterinary surgeon during her last week of pregnancy. He may be able to give you some indication when she is likely to come into labour. He may also advise worming if the bitch has not already been wormed. It may be relevant to emphasize that worming should always be carried out before the bitch is mated and again after the forty-first day of pregnancy. Modern worm remedies are very safe and with some it is now usual to administer low daily or weekly doses throughout pregnancy and while the puppies are suckling until they are weaned. Maiden bitches vary considerably in their whelping behaviour. Some go to full term and whelp easily. Many will whimper, tear their blankets, scratch feverishly and make their beds, or rush wildly from room to room one or two days before their litters arrive. Some try to find a secret place for their lying-in. You must be prepared for all these tricks. Don't be misled by such antics into believing that the bitch is about to whelp at once. This behaviour may go on for hours or the whole day previous to parturition.

Signs that the Whelping is Imminent

One of the earliest indications that labour may be anticipated within 24 to 48 hours is a drop in the bitch's temperature, although this is often not seen. Thereafter the following signs should be looked for and noted; they are all pointers that actual whelping will not be long delayed:

(1) The bitch settles down rather quietly, often stretched full out with head between paws.
(2) She pants and breathes heavily, perhaps giving a sharp cry as though in pain; these are the labour pains.
(3) She makes apprehensive turns of her head, looking anxiously at her rear parts.
(4) She will refuse food.
(5) She will more often than not vomit.
(6) The vulva is swollen and softens, and there is a clear mucous discharge.
(7) She will press hard with her rear against her box and make heaving or straining motions.

No. 7 is the most important sign of all, and at the first sign of straining you should look at your watch. The time elapsing between these first heaves and the delivery, or more specifically the non-appearance of a whelp, tells you whether the whelping is going to be quite normal or whether you may expect difficulty. It is the most important phase in intelligent co-operation with the veterinary surgeon if a complication ensues, and the information which will help him most. Invariably the veterinary surgeon's first question is: 'When did she actually start in labour?' If you cannot accurately inform him he has to guess. If you can tell him 'three, four or five hours ago', he can more readily decide what action to take.

The Biological Factors, and Normal Course of an Uncomplicated Whelping

Labour straining having started, the intermittent heaves may continue for anything from five minutes to one and a half hours before a pup is produced. These should be followed by the appearance of the water-bag (a lay expression; the following is a technical description). The water-bag should not be mistaken for a whelp, as is so frequently done by novices (see Figure 3). It resembles a mass of greenish-black fluid contained in a membrane or skin; it varies in size according to the time taken to pass it. Each foetal whelp is encased in a membrane, and contained in a sac of fluid. This is designed by nature to protect the whelp while in the uterus or womb from external shock or injury as it acts like a buffer or cushion. A further purpose of this amniotic fluid sac is that instead of the whelp's body emerging first, the uterine contractions squeeze the fluid into a bag-shape, which by preceding the whelp facilitates its egress, having gently dilated the vaginal passage.

The way for the whelp thus prepared, the water-bag emerges and bursts, and a whelp *should* shortly afterwards appear, either nose first with front feet facing forward or hind legs first since both anterior and posterior presentation (this is not a breech!) are normal in the bitch. One vigorous labour strain will usually expel the whelp immediately and entirely.

The whelp is still deriving nourishment and oxygen via the umbilical cord, which attaches it to the placenta. The placenta, commonly known as the afterbirth, resembles a mass of raw meat, and varies in size from two inches in diameter to five inches according to the breed.

Cord and placenta should both come away with the whelp (see Figure 5, page 83). The whelp being completely encased in the membrane, the normal bitch's instinct and immediate duty is to tear away this membrane with her teeth, thus allowing the whelp to breathe air for the first time in the post-uterine state. Next, the bitch should start to sever

Figure 3 The water-bag presenting

Anterior presentation

Posterior presentation

Note hindlegs are not
stretched out

Breech presentation

Figure 4 The anterior, posterior and breech presentations

with her teeth the umbilical cord and finally devour the after-birth. This is a normal function; it provides the bitch with some nourishment, so that she may take no solid food during the first forty-eight hours. She should next energetically lick the pup and generally rough house it all over the whelping bed; this is to dry and warm it and to stimulate the heart action and lungs. By this time the whelp should have given its first tiny cry; when that happens one knows all is well, and in a few minutes it should fumble towards a nipple and start guzzling. The bitch heaves a sigh, settles her head between her paws, and awaits the next onset of pains, which should occur within half an hour and should never be delayed by more than three hours. The whole process is repeated again and is continued until all the whelps have arrived, when the bitch settles herself down. The breathing is calm, deep and slow again; the anxious, strained look disappears. She takes on a seraphic expression and has no further use for her master or mistress for at least two days, merely tolerating their presence. She violently resents intrusion by anyone else. A curtain should be put over the box. Keep her quiet and in semi-darkness, and withstand the temptation to show her puppies to all and sundry, since this can not only upset the bitch but also increase the chances of infections, if the bitch is due for a booster against the inoculable diseases which would mean the puppies receiving a reasonable level of maternal antibodies through her milk. The bitch is frequently thirsty at this stage and should be given drinks of warm milk with added glucose, or gravy and eggs if she prefers. Many authorities suggest no solid food should be given for forty-eight hours after whelping but there is no foundation for this theory. If the bitch is hungry after her massive exertions she should be fed but care should be taken not to overdo it within the first forty-eight hours when she well may have diarrhoea as a result of eating her afterbirths.

Try to weigh each puppy as it is born.

Post natal examination It is not always easy to ascertain whether the last or all the puppies have arrived. By feeling the flanks, foetal movements can sometimes be detected. It is to the advantage of all breeders, particularly the novice, to have a post-natal veterinary examination, preferably within twenty-four hours of the whelping. This is, firstly to ensure that no whelp has been left unborn (which can cause dire complications when one had thought all was well), and, secondly, the veterinary surgeon will give an injection to clear the uterus of any afterbirth or membrane debris remaining. This reduces the risk of temperature from a septic condition and ultimate septicaemia.

Note that throughout the whole of this normal whelping the owner should merely sit beside the bitch; his presence and occasional soft-toned encouragement will give her all the assistance she requires. In a

THE WHELP STILL —
ENCLOSED IN MEMBRANE   THE CORD

THE PLACENTA
OR "AFTER BIRTH"

Figure 5 A whelp and afterbirth delivered

normal whelping as above described let your policy be: minimum amount of interference or assistance; know what she should do and act only if she fails to do it; know what complications to expect and act correctly when they happen. If the bitch behaves normally, and nothing untoward occurs, leave her alone; don't agitate her. It is important not to display anxiety and fuss too much over her during the forty-eight hours before the due date. Animals can sense such concern and react to it.

Later chapters will give you the knowledge you require, and help you to decide whether the whelping is normal or complicated, or whether your interference is required.

Chapter 9

General remarks on abnormal whelpings—How to minimize possible complications—Some statistics

AN abnormal whelping may be expected if the bitch strains continuously for two to three hours with no sign of a birth. Here a veterinary surgeon's immediate attendance is strongly advised (having previously warned him of the whelping). It is not meant that a lapse of three hours necessarily indicates disaster, but it might, therefore no time should be lost in securing expert assistance. If just before the veterinary surgeon arrives a beautiful pup does pop out comfortably, so much the better, but if there is a serious complication, such as a lateral deviation of the head at the brim of the pelvis, how glad you will be that the veterinary surgeon is on his way to deal with it! He will remove the first whelp. Your bitch is still fresh and strong—ready to settle down to deliver the next. If, on the other hand, the bitch is left unaided she will strain repeatedly, trying hard, but will so tire herself that her muscles will become exhausted and she will either pack up because she is lazy and will not exert herself further, or because from sheer pain she is incapable of further effort. The result may be the death of all the whelps and possibly of the bitch herself. Early removal of the cause of the trouble is essential; whether the offending pup be delivered alive or dead, you may save all the others and preserve your bitch's life.

It is emphasized that this 'over three hours' lapse' refers not merely to the arrival of the first whelp; it is equally applicable after the delivery of *each* whelp. As each whelp is delivered look at your watch and make a mental note: 'If the next water-bag does not arrive in three hours from now I will call in the vet.' Perhaps this is even more important than with the arrival of the first. Let us study a simple example. The bitch is perfectly fit; she has strained for fifteen minutes and pup number one pops out, suckles, and the bitch lies contentedly. Half an hour passes and a few heaves produce another lovely pup. Similarly, after a further half-hour pup three is delivered. You are now elatedly gloating over their perfection. The bitch, however, by her behaviour obviously has at least one or two more whelps to come. She is restless, seems a little in pain, is rather tired now, and although she has made some straining efforts for the last two hours she will not exert herself to the full and appears not to relish the thought of producing this one, and looks as if she is going to pack up. A further hour has gone by but nothing has happened. This may be all right; on the other hand, it may be all wrong. Don't take a chance on it; ring your veterinary surgeon. It may be two or more hours before he comes, during which time your bitch's chances are decreasing if she has a major complication, or a minor one beyond your skill. When he arrives he can end the complication, or take whatever course he deems advisable. Your bitch is still fairly strong for the remainder; the earlier arrivals will not be orphaned and the following ones may be whelped simply. Take the converse picture: if you go to bed when only three whelps have been delivered, feeling 'she will have had the rest by the morning', you may find her dead, her lovely pups weakening from lack of her care.

Before dealing in detail with minor and major complications, their recognition and treatment, it will be expedient to give some statistics and a classification ranging from normal whelpings to the most severe and fatal issues.

Study of at least a thousand cases would be necessary before a completely reliable analysis could be made. The writer actually did appeal to other breeders to send him reports, on the lines of the classification below, of their whelping cases. From these he intended to collect and collate sufficient data to make possible a summary from which could be accurately gauged the percentage of normal to abnormal whelpings, with the intermediate degrees. The response was so poor, however, that he has had to rely largely on his own experience, which, with the few others reported, covers approximately a hundred whelping cases. Therefore no claim is made that the following statements are indisputable; they should be regarded as a rough guide only, taken from experience up to the 1950s.

Normal whelpings; bitches and all whelps healthy and all survived	50 per cent
Whelpings with minor complications but bitch and all whelps survived	27 "
Whelpings with major complications, where bitch survived but some or all whelps were lost	20 "
Whelpings with major complications where bitch died and some or all of the whelps died	3 "

From this analysis two facts stand out. Firstly, that in one of every four litters there will be some complication causing the loss or death of whelps; secondly, that one bitch will die in approximately every thirty whelpings.

It is the first fact that so impressed the writer that it induced him to publish this book, in the hope that breeders, by gaining a deeper knowledge of the intricacies of whelping, can reduce the incidence of whelp mortality. On the other hand, the bitch mortality of 3 per cent can be regarded as low and encouraging, but the significant fact here is that at practically all the whelpings on which this analysis is based SOMEONE SAT IN ATTENDANCE FROM START TO FINISH, AND THROUGHOUT EACH THERE WAS INTELLIGENT CO-OPERATION WITH THE VETERINARY SURGEON WHEN NECESSARY. One is convinced beyond a shadow of doubt that had this not been done in many of the 25 per cent cases of major complications more bitches would have been lost, and the bitch mortality rate would have been much higher. [These results accrued by Captain Graham refer to the 1940s and 1950s. Today survival rates are much higher and to lose a bitch as a result of whelping is very rare indeed.] The so-called natural method of whelping can fairly be described as nothing short of cruelty—where the bitch is just left in some outhouse to get on with it and only on the next morning visited, possibly to find one or two born dead puppies (and probably unnecessarily so) or the bitch in dire distress and danger. The dog is no longer a wild animal living in the natural state when it preferred to whelp alone. It is a domesticated animal, and its accouchement calls for unstinted care. This does not mean coddling, over-interference or over-fussing. In many whelpings the writer has been connected with the bitch would not attempt to whelp alone, and became frenzied if left, obviously beseeching someone to see her through.

So intense is the affection of a bitch for her master at whelping time that situations can become embarrassing and unmentionable in polite or non-doggy circles. The author's most typical experience of this was an occasion when a camp bed had been placed in the whelping shed on which to relax while waiting and watching. Whenever he left the shed the bitch screamed as if demented. In the small hours the bitch jumped on his chest and, with no due warning, there deposited her first whelp. A messy business, but if one loves one's dogs a lot must be forgiven. Having cleaned up the whelp, it was returned with its mother to the whelping box where both remained contentedly for an hour. She then, with the whelp in her mouth, again jumped on his chest, pushed the whelp against his hand with her nose, and with an expression of 'you look after this' proceeded to deposit another whelp in exactly the same place. Having resignedly changed his attire for the second time he wondered how he could obviate a repetition. He couldn't. This procedure occurred five times; before each birth the bitch leaped from her box, each time with a whelp in her mouth and each time pushing it towards a hand, and delivering the next whelp on the one spot she had definitely decided was the only right one. Such is the faith, persistence, affection and obstinacy of the Dachshund. The foregoing is not fictitious narrative; it was unfortunately for the author, only too true.

On another occasion while sitting in front of the kitchen fire for a winter whelping, another bitch could not be induced to deposit her whelps anywhere else than on the author's lap as each one arrived. Other breeders can recount similar experiences of this devotion and trust.

Chapter 10

Minor complications in detail—How to act when professional aid is not available—Severance of the cord—Breech presentation—Uterine inertia

In this chapter complications are detailed and advice given about action in emergencies. Step by step, we will consider MINOR complications at each stage of normal whelpings.

(1) A bitch is lazy and nervous; feeling pain and having made a tentative heave, she cries and will make no further labour effort, knowing it will hurt. She will lie passively, sulk, and pack it up. This has been known to go on for twelve hours and calls for veterinary action; an injection has to be given to contract the uterus and expel the whelp, or the whelps must be removed with forceps. Technically, this is an example of uterine inertia.

(2) The water-bag appears, bursts, but is not followed by a whelp. If a period of more than two hours elapses some complication must be feared, especially if the bitch continues to strain heavily. A veterinary surgeon must always be contacted after this period.

(3) The bitch, particularly a maiden one, when the first whelp appears either has no instinct to attend to her immediate duties or is too frightened to do so. Here you must assist. It is essential that the membrane covering the whelp is removed to allow it to breathe. Pull away the membrane from the head and strip it from the whelp. Also separate the whelp from the placenta—that is, sever the cord. You must take care to avoid one of the chief causes of an umbilical hernia. An umbilical hernia is a protrusion of the gut through the abdominal wall at the region where the cord from the placenta is attached to the whelp. Faulty manipulation here will put a strain on the abdominal muscles and cause a hernia (see Figure 6). The correct way to ensure that this does not occur is: Pinch the cord in the thumb and forefinger of the right hand about one inch from the whelp's body, pinch the cord between the thumb and forefinger of the left hand, with the thumbs of each hand touching. Pull with your RIGHT hand, i.e. pull the pup away from your left hand; NEVER pull the cord from the whelp's body. The average cord will sever after a twist and pull; if it is unduly tough, cut the cord with a pair of sterilized scissors approximately one inch from the body;

Figure 6 The severance of the umbilical cord. Arrow shows the right hand pulling away from the left

squeezing the cord between the thumb and forefinger for approximately thirty seconds usually stops any bleeding. However, you can ligature the cord using sterile thread. Warm the puppy by rubbing it with a towel which is placed in your hand with the puppy on it, using another piece of towel to rub against your hand, just lightly touching the puppy. This stimulates the pup and warms it by friction although it is your hand and not the puppy that is taking most of the force of the rubbing.

Figure 7 The appearance of a posterior presentation. Both feet have been presented or worked out with the fingers

Afterwards place it to a nipple. It will probably give its first cry and this usually induces the bitch to begin licking and tending it.

(4) *The posterior presentation* When the puppy comes backwards, tail and hindlegs are being delivered first and this is popularly known as the breech presentation. Strictly it is a posterior presentation, which is relatively common in the bitch (see Figure 7). Complications are unlikely to develop provided the puppy is expelled fairly rapidly. As soon as the puppy passes into the birth canal its blood supply via the afterbirth is cut off and therefore it must be born relatively quickly or else it will die of lack of oxygen. The bitch will often deliver a posterior presentation totally unaided but it is a wise precaution to assist her in order to ensure a rapid birth. Using a piece of tissue or a clean towel, gently grasp the legs, tail or hindquarters that are protruding and pull with steady gentle traction at approximately 45° to the bitch (see Figure 8).

The true breech presentation is a major complication which does occur in the bitch but not very frequently. Here the hindlegs are forward and the puppy's tail and rump are all that is presented (see Figure 4 on page 81). This makes the puppy much more difficult to deliver and even

Figure 8 The posterior presentation being delivered. First stage. The feet are now grasped firmly in cotton wool

Figure 9 The final delivery of a breech whelp. Arrow indicates downward and outward pull

91

a really good whelping bitch will often exhaust herself by her abortive efforts to expel it. The uterine muscles then tire and during the delay another whelp can pass down the uterine horn and further block the birth.

Action: Get the bitch on a table. If you have an assistant get him to hold the bitch's head firmly under his arm, placing the right hand (if he is right-handed) under the abdomen and with gentle pressure raise it; at the same time he can use his left fingers to stretch the lips of the vulva. With a piece of tissue or cotton wool to counteract the slipperiness, grasp whatever is presented and gently pull at 45° (see Figure 9). If it is a true breech and there is only a tail presented, you may find that you will have to insert a well-scrubbed finger into the vagina to try to hook back the hind legs which are pointed forward. Once you have got hold of them, do not let go otherwise they are likely to slip back within the bitch beyond reach. Do not jerk when the bitch strains but keep up a steady traction which will stimulate her to help you by pushing, centimetre by centimetre. As the puppy is expelled you can work up the body, taking a firmer grip. The puppy has got to come out and ringing the veterinary surgeon at this stage will only create more delay. Therefore do not be afraid, grasp firmly and pull firmly, but do not tug.

Note that emphasis is laid on the necessity for minimum delay in a breech delivery. If the envelope covering the whelp happens to be torn and the whelp's head is uncovered it can't breathe and after a few minutes in this condition it will die. Or fluid may enter its nostrils and it is drowned. It is better to get the breech puppy away, dead or alive, in order to save the whelps to come, and possibly the bitch. If prolonged, the whelp may be very weak and half dead; therefore sever the cord, clear the membrane, open the mouth with your little finger, draw forward the tongue, blow or breathe into the mouth. Swinging the whelp up and down is also very useful. When you hear the first whimper you will enjoy the thrill of achievement, of having successfully delivered your first breech. This may sound difficult to the inexperienced. In practice it is well within the capability of the novice, and after one or two cases it becomes simple.

(5) An abnormally large whelp, stuck half way; the bitch won't try to expel it further and runs about with the whelp hanging. Again prompt action is required. It is similar in many respects to the breech delivery, except that the whelp being head first makes the task easier and there is less chance of the feet getting snagged. Although the head is exposed, and you will have cleared the membrane, the whelp still cannot breathe, as its lungs are compressed by the restricted space; consequently speed, as in the case of the breech delivery, is equally necessary here.

Wait for the intermittent straining by the bitch and work your right finger round the whelp at each strain with a drawing down motion, pushing apart the lips of the vagina (vulva) with the fingers of the other hand. If unsuccessful after a quarter of an hour, SOS your veterinary surgeon.

(6) The after-birth not coming away with the whelp, and only a small portion of cord exposed.

Action: Sever what there is of the cord exposed, as explained at (3), and proceed similarly with the whelp. This condition does not call for urgent veterinary attention, but you should always tell your veterinary surgeon that the after-birth was not passed. At his routine visit after the whelping he will inject a drug which will cause the uterus to contract, and so expel the after-birth and evacuate from the uterus any membranes left behind.

(7) A bitch is sometimes too fat or too heavy in whelp, and when a pup has arrived she cannot reach her end part to perform her immediate duties. Here you must do them for her as already described.

Chapter 11

The last chapter described certain complications which can be successfully dealt with without the aid of a veterinary surgeon, if one is not available.

There are, however, more severe types, treatment for which is quite beyond the capabilities of anyone other than a skilled surgeon. The reader need not be alarmed or imagine that any of them occur frequently, but a brief description is advisable as it should be known that they MAY happen. Such knowledge should result in intelligent co-operation with the veterinary surgeon, the theme of Part II of this book.

A major complication is always a possibility if nothing has happened after three hours of real labour heaves. If veterinary assistance is likely to be long delayed, or unobtainable, assistance may be attempted by the owner by inserting a finger right up the vagina and into the pelvis and endeavouring to twist, turn and work the whelp over the brim of the pelvis, or clear whatever obstruction is there. Complete sterilization and scrupulous cleanliness is vitally necessary whenever a novice makes a digital exploration of the vaginal passage. If subsequently a Caesarean section has to be performed dirty manipulation would cause a septic condition which would seriously affect the post-operative result. Therefore, wash the bitch's hind parts with soap and water, and whenever the fingers are inserted into the vagina the hands should first have been thoroughly sterilized with suitable disinfectant and water and the fingers smeared with medicated Vaseline.

Examples of Some Types of Major Complications

(1) Lateral deviation of the head. Instead of the nose passing over the brim of the pelvis the head is turned sideways and the neck only is against the orifice. All labour movements of the bitch aggravate the condition. Injections to stimulate the bitch would be absolutely wrong in this situation, as contracting movements would tend to dislocate the

neck and tire the bitch. The veterinary surgeon is frequently able to turn the head and deliver the whelp with forceps, or by Caesarean. In this way that puppy and the others may be saved.

(2) Two whelps presenting at the same time down each horn, meeting simultaneously at the exit of the pelvis and becoming 'locked'. Pretty grim, and a sound argument for warning a veterinary surgeon at the three-hour period, as previously emphasized.

(3) Three whelps presenting simultaneously and getting entangled. Grimmer still, and only an operation can relieve. The writer had this experience with a $6\frac{1}{2}$-lb. Miniature. Only two had presented together at first, and while working on these a third presented itself to mess things up even more—a tangled mass of three whelps over the pelvic brim. The veterinary surgeon had never had this complication before. He could do nothing on the spot; it was a case of a shot of morphia, hot water bottles, a dash by car to his operating table, and operative removal. All the whelps were lost, the bitch was terribly ill for three days after the severe manipulations but pulled through, and afterwards was a first-prize winner again, and promoted from the Kennels to be one of the house dogs as a reward for her pluck. Had she been left unattended in an outhouse from the start of this whelping till morning, her suffering would have been terrible and she would have died.

(4) The puppy presents upside down. This is a very difficult complication. Normally the back should be uppermost with the head and rump turning downwards and towards each other, and in this position the whelp slides comfortably over the pelvic brim. With the complication of the belly uppermost, with either a head or a breech presentation, when the bitch strains the puppy is forced upwards against the roof of the pelvis. They can rarely be delivered without veterinary help.

(5) The front legs and feet facing backward and tucked on the chest, instead of forward under the nose. This increases the girth or bulk of the whelp in the region of its chest and impedes smooth delivery. Treatment is as for minor complication number 5 until the veterinary surgeon arrives.

(6) A true breech presentation when the feet, instead of presenting, are tucked under the belly and only the rump or tail appears at the vaginal exit. A rather nasty case, but it can be dealt with by drawing the feet to their correct position, then bringing out one foot and then the other and proceeding as for the simple, uncomplicated posterior presentation.

(7) A fortunately fairly rare condition is when the backbone lodges across the orifice of the pelvis, and digital examination contacts only the back. It is a worse condition than lateral deviation of the head, and

veterinary skill deals with it in much the same way as for that complication.

It is hoped that advice given so far in this book has made out a case for the necessity of being with your bitch at whelping time, and has shown some of the calamities that can happen if you leave her unattended. Not only is your presence humane; such attachment to your bitch will also prove profitable to your Kennel account. An owner not prepared to give this care should not breed.

Chapter 12

Complications which may affect the bitch after whelping—Conditions which can receive home treatment—The importance of knowledge of temperature

Complications after Whelping

(1) *Mastitis* or Mammitis, meaning an inflammatory condition of the mammary glands, or breasts. This is by no means uncommon and is caused by the milk not being extracted from one or more glands. It may happen whether whelps are or are not left with the dam. In the former case the whelps appear to ignore one or more glands, sucking only from a few of the teats. The trouble may be detected by the bitch being restless and off her food, and by her high temperature. The glands and nipples affected are swollen and appear to contain hard lumps; they are hot, reddish-purple, distended and very tender. The condition can be very acute and a veterinary surgeon's advice should always be sought when puppies are avoiding any teats which appear hot or painful. Gentle massage and the application of warm flannels in an attempt to draw off some of the milk is a good first-aid measure until the veterinary surgeon sees the bitch. It is always worthwhile taking the bitch's temperature, since with acute mastitis the bitch can quite suddenly become extremely ill with a temperature of 103°F or more. Occasionally, despite the use of broad spectrum antibiotics, abscessation will occur and the veterinary surgeon may advise hot fomentations. If the abscess bursts a quite horrifying amount of bloodstained pus will suddenly run out and the cavity left can be quite huge. However, do not panic, the bitch will be a lot better after this has occurred, the painful period being during the development of the abscess. Her temperature will quickly return to normal and she will contentedly continue to feed her puppies who will suck quite near to the gaping hole! It is important that veterinary instructions regarding bathing, antibiotics etc. are strictly followed. Modern broad spectrum antibiotics will bring about a rapid healing of the abscess. Things used to be very different before these wonder drugs were available. [As an example, an experience quoted by Captain Portman-Graham in earlier editions of this book has been retained for

comparison.]

An authentic experience, with the course of treatment described, will give an instructive example of the veterinary advice and the correct method of carrying out treatment. The case involved a Miniature bitch, weighing barely six pounds. She whelped two puppies seven days too soon. They were too immature to live and died eight hours after birth. Here it was reasonable to suppose that mastitis might occur. A day later another bad whelping case occurred with a six-and-a-half-years-old Standard Smooth Dachshund, which proved fatal after Caesarean section—this being only the second whelping fatality in an experience of over twenty years. As a result of the Standard's Caesarean two moribund orphan pups were brought back from the vet's and hand-reared for twenty-four hours. We then tried to see if the Miniature bitch would suckle the orphaned Standard whelps; such an arrangement would be good for the bitch, to avoid mastitis, and would enable the pups to have natural bitch's milk. She took to them instantly and for three days all went splendidly. We then observed mastitis symptoms and the first-aid treatment already described was carried out, but we could draw off no trace of milk from one extremely hard and tender gland. The temperature had risen to 105 degrees and an abscess had appeared. We now deemed it wise to seek immediate assistance from our veterinary surgeon, and under his supervision the following treatment was carried out.

With continued hot fomentations the abscess was induced to burst, but the remaining condition had to be treated. First the wound was kept scrupulously clean by bathing with hot water hourly. Every two hours the hole was irrigated with acriflavine, 1 in 1,000 solution, and after each wet treatment the wound was left covered with a thick dusting of M and B powder. Temperature dropped and general condition improved. After three days of the treatment, with the abscess cavity clearing up well, the mammary gland tissue was protruding from the hole. This was all removed with a sharp pair of scissors. The acriflavine and M and B powder treatment was continued for a week, the edges of the cavity gradually approximated and complete healing took place. When it is realized that at the worst period the abscess sac was big enough to take a bantam's egg, was raw, purulent and the sloughed gland was exfoliating from it, it will be understood that mastitis can develop into a serious condition. However, if at the more serious stage the veterinary surgeon takes over and his advice is carefully followed no alarm need be felt. Provided one knows the correct procedure and treatment from early recognition to ultimate cure, the joy of success is ample reward for the time and patience bestowed. This instance is the most impressive in my experience of the guts and toughness which some maternal bitches will display when rearing whelps. With something so tiny fostering two Standard pups, at six weeks old nearly as big as their foster-mother, who for about a week was desperately ill and in intense pain, with the lusty pups sucking all the time close to a gaping, painful wound, and proving a zealous and jealous mother, we have an astonishing example of canine grit of the highest type. This bitch never looked back and is as fit and sound (although minus one mammary gland) as one could desire. As a reward she became a favourite house pet, instead of a kennel inmate. The orphaned whelps of the other bitch thrived beautifully, and one became the winner of a CC and two Reserve CCs.

(2) *Metritis*, or inflammation of the uterus, is not an uncommon complication of parturition. It can be caused by bruising or a reduction in the bitch's resistance due to chilling or exposure to cold after whelping by retained foetal membranes or afterbirth or by the unsuspected presence of a dead whelp. It may result from a protracted labour, dirty manipulation with fingers or instruments or roughness. Sometimes tears occur in the lining to the passage during birth and this can be the source of the trouble. The main signs are a pus-stained reddish or brown discharge, lack of appetite, dullness, and usually a raised temperature. In very acute cases, collapse, coma and death can ensue.

Metritis is an acute veterinary emergency. Even if the bitch's life is not in danger, her milk supply certainly will be if she runs a fever. All the novice can or should do is to have enough knowledge to diagnose the condition. The symptoms described will help him in this respect. He may administer a laxative, as the bowels must be kept loose, and keep the patient very warm until the veterinary surgeon takes over.

(3) *Milk fever* or *eclampsia* usually occurs when milk supplies are at their peak, usually two to three weeks after whelping, although cases are known where the condition has occurred prior to whelping. It is not due to an overall lack of calcium but a lack of calcium in the bloodstream due to the heavy demands caused by lactation. It is always the really good Mum, loving and nursing her children with a super abundance of milk that is the victim. Small breeds, Poodles, Yorkshire Terriers etc. are relatively more prone than the larger breeds except those with very large litters.

Panting is probably the first sign, with a look of apprehension on the bitch's face. If she is moved she frequently will appear to walk with a stiff-legged gait and that is the time to call the veterinary surgeon. Very quickly she will be off her legs and eclamptic convulsions or fits can very soon occur. This is one of the few real emergencies in small animal practice and it is for this reason that it is always worth contacting your veterinary surgeon at the time of whelping, letting him carry out a post-natal examination and discussing the possibilities of milk fever with him. At least then he will be forewarned if there is a panic call at 3 a.m. because the bitch has gone off her legs!

Treatment is usually very spectacular but does involve injections of a calcium product. No amount of extra calcium by mouth will affect the condition. Some bitches appear to be extremely prone and can have several attacks while nursing. In such a case it is better either to hand rear the puppies and dry off the bitch or at least supplement them to ensure there is not this sudden drop in calcium blood level.

(4) *Early cessation of milk supply* Detect in good time and hand-feed. The whelps will give you the warning by crying continuously. Contented whelps rarely cry. Wean the whelps much earlier than under normal conditions.

Temperature

Every novice may not know that a dog's temperature is not the same as that of a human. The normal canine temperature is 101·5 degrees, or nearly three degrees higher than in man. Thus a temperature of 102·5 degrees in a dog one would regard as slight, 104 degrees as high, and 105 to 106 degrees as very high to dangerous. As dogs cannot tell us when they are ill, the thermometer should be considered a most important piece of equipment which no Kennel should be without. It is our chief aid to diagnosis. Without it we should be quite unaware of the necessity of calling in a veterinary surgeon, if no other symptoms are apparent. So if one has a dog looking a little off colour and there are no symptoms at all, take the temperature as a routine measure. If the temperature is 102·5 or more seek veterinary advice at once. The ordinary clinical half-minute thermometer is used. It is first soaped or greased, then inserted into the rectum for about one inch. No force is needed, and dogs seldom resist, but the thermometer must be held in place firmly for from half to one minute to prevent it dropping out and breaking.

In cases of a nervous dog who does resist, control is gained by holding its tail firmly, then getting the animal between your arm and your body to steady it, holding its back legs with your left hand at the same time.

Chapter 13

Dealing with newly born puppies—Complications which may affect pups after whelping—Hernia, its avoidance and home-treatment—Revival of a moribund whelp—Rearing orphaned whelps—How to introduce a foster-mother

Revival of apparently dead whelps An early experience may make so strong an impression that it remains to influence one's subsequent actions. An incident is clearly recalled that made the writer realize that though a whelp may appear to be dead it can be resurrected, and taught him never to give up hope until all possible remedies have been tried. It happened in this way.

Circumstances had prevented the writer, then a novice, from being present when one of his first Scottie bitches was whelping. When he could attend her the bitch was in great distress and almost unconscious. Two puppies had been born three hours previously, but the bitch had buried them in the sacking and they were dead. They looked so dead that he wrapped them in paper intending later to place them in the incinerator. On arrival of the veterinary surgeon the dead pups were mentioned and he asked to see them. The conversation took place in front of the kitchen fire and, while one whelp was being held up for the vet to examine it gave an almost imperceptible shudder, and there was the faintest movement of a claw. This was due to the combination of warmth from a hand and from the fire. The vet said: 'You've got a live pup there—put it in the oven.' Cotton wool was quickly put in a cardboard box, both pups put in, and it was placed in an oven probably hot enough to cook a meal. After only a minute or two movements were seen from both pups; later they were actually wriggling. In the meantime the vet was dealing with the bitch (a piecemeal removal of the offending whelp with the complication of lateral deviation of the head), while the writer alternately rubbed the pups and held them close to the fire. The bitch fairly soon regained strength. Her intense pain having been relieved, she took an interest in the pups, licked them, and within two hours they had enough strength to attach themselves to a nipple. Both lived and one was ultimately shown.

After that the writer has never thought a whelp dead until he knew it to be very dead.

The cause in the case referred to was quite simple—lack of attention from bitch or human, and exposure to cold.

With any of the major or minor complications already described, as for example a protracted and delayed breech, or where there has been undue compression on the lungs, a whelp when it is ultimately delivered will look lifeless. They are usually cold, long and drawn out, thin and flat, and appear so lifeless that they apparently have about as much chance of survival as the proverbial snowball in hell. Many such cases can be brought to life, though the inexperienced might reasonably have considered the whelps dead.

The following routine methods can be tried before the whelp is relegated to the dustbin. The thrill of seeing a movement or hearing a faint squeak in successful cases repays one for the trouble taken; it is a joy which must be experienced to be appreciated.

(1) Open the mouth and insert the little finger, very gently depress the tongue, blow down the mouth, or, holding the mouth close to one's own, breathe steadily in and out several times. Try to draw the tongue backwards and forwards using a clean finger. This movement being gentle and regular corresponds to normal breathing.

(2) Into a bowl place some hot water (obviously not so hot as to scald the whelp) and immerse the whelp right up to its neck for a minute or two.

(3) For at least five minutes vigorously massage over the heart and lung area, and rub quickly to induce friction on the whole of the whelp's body.

(4) Hold the whelp very close to a source of heat, turning it round so that the heat penetrates all parts of the body.

(5) Hold the whelp's head in your right hand and the body in your left. Raise it to the height of your shoulder, then with a gentle swinging motion bring it down to the level of your knee. A violent movement is not necessary. This will often cause the heart to start beating.

(6) One drop of brandy or other alcohol placed on the tongue sometimes stimulates the puppy to take a breath.

If as a result of any or all of these measures you see signs of life continue your efforts with renewed energy; if life is present you can maintain it.

To sum up, many of the apparently born dead pups one hears of so frequently can be converted into live pups (and future CC winners) if some of the steps indicated are taken promptly.

Hernia, its prevention and treatment. How to avoid it The subject of umbilical hernia could have been included in a later chapter, among the complications affecting the whelp after birth, but since one of its main causes can occur actually at whelping it will be more fitting to describe it and its treatment in a separate section at this stage. Its definition was given in Chapter 10, where it was shown that anyone tending the bitch might cause a hernia through faulty manipulation, and the correct method was described. The second cause of umbilical hernia at whelping time is similar, but caused by the bitch. Some bitches, through fright or over-zealousness, attack the cord almost ferociously, and with one paw on the whelp will snatch and tear at the cord, and by tugging instead of quickly biting will draw the guts from the whelp's abdomen. If you observe this, intervene at once, soothe the bitch, and sever the cord for her in the correct manner already detailed.

The following method has been practised successfully: A piece of cork approximately the size of a 2p piece and approximately a quarter of an inch thick can be bound over the hernia using wide Elastoplast. Ensure there is a piece of cotton wool between the hernia and the cork. The tape must not be tight enough to restrict the abdomen at all, but sufficiently firm to put pressure on the cork to transmit it to the hernia. Some puppies will tolerate this bandage even at a very young age, others are distressed and it should then be removed. Another factor to contend with is the bitch who may become very agitated if a puppy is treated in this way. Again the only answer is to remove the dressing. In puppies of one to two weeks old the cork need only be kept in position for about forty-eight hours and there will be considerable improvement. The reason for this is that the protruding gut is enlarging the traumatic opening in the weakened abdominal wall and if the protrusion is eliminated the torn abdominal muscles will automatically heal very rapidly. With older puppies (up to three months) a similar method can be tried, although in most cases a surgical operation is then necessary. If in doubt consult your vet.

Prolapse of Anus This is an eversion, or turning outwards, of the lower part of the rectum, and is caused in very young whelps by straining to pass faeces. Its appearance is that of an enlarged, very red fleshy mass from a quarter to a half inch protruding outside. This must be immediately reduced by pressing it back again with wet cotton wool, repeating the pressure every time there is a recurrence. If straining is due to constipation as evidenced by the lack of any faeces or a big fat 'belly' a few drops of liquid paraffin by mouth may help resolve the situation. However, most cases of prolapse of the anus are due to an ongoing enteritis and liquid paraffin in these cases will only exacerbate the situation. The condition calls for an expert opinion as soon as possible:

therefore call the vet. In the meantime, try to keep the part clean and moist using saline solution. The puppy should be removed from the bitch who will invariably endeavour to clean and chew at the prolapsed part if she is not prevented. Until seen by the veterinary surgeon, it is essential that the prolapsed area is kept moist.

Milk Rash Ocassionally puppies develop allergies due to the bitch's milk. The hair may come away in patches and dry flaky scabs appear and scale off. This can also occur at weaning time when other protein foods are being introduced. If the puppy is still suckling from the bitch, try weaning on to other forms of protein. If the puppy is already off the bitch, discontinue the present formula and consult your veterinary surgeon regarding alternative nourishment.

Eye Trouble Failure to open at normal time, runny or watery eyes, conjunctivitis, matter formation and tendency for lids to stick together, pus formation with a large bulge under the lid. In any of the above conditions simple first aid is to bathe regularly with cold water. Any eye problem with a young puppy should be mentioned to the veterinary surgeon as soon as possible.

Intussusception This is invagination of the bowel, or more simply a telescoping of one part of the bowel into another. It is not uncommon in young whelps up to eight weeks old, and is often present at the same time as a prolapsed anus. Symptons are lack of appetite, marked abdominal distension, vomiting, rise in temperature, bloodstained and jelly-like discharge, crying out in pain, and marked tenderness on palpating the abdomen. Worms can often be a cause and with modern worm remedies it is worth worming the puppies from fourteen days onwards. If the puppy is gravely ill the veterinary surgeon should be contacted immediately. Modern anaesthesia means that operation to remove the intussusception or resect part of the bowel carries an encouraging success rate, even in very young puppies.

Deformities Hare lip, obvious malformation of joints or limbs, the latter being unequal in size, either elongated or shortened. Always follow your veterinary surgeon's advice. These deformed puppies are often a burden, not only to themselves but to you as they develop and, although upsetting, euthanasia is often the wisest course.

Inability to suckle This may arise from a variety of causes, but whatever the cause carry on as for orphaned whelp, described below, until normal suckling can be induced.

Rearing Orphaned Whelps

Briefly, the essentials are time, patience and perseverance. A whelp must receive some nourishment within three hours of birth. Today

Lactol,* Welpi** and other simulated bitch's milk preparations are available and the manufacturers' instructions regarding reconstitution should be carefully followed. Anyone contemplating a litter should previously provide themselves with a premature baby feeder (Belcroy) which can be obtained from most veterinary surgeons or a Catac open-ended feeder specifically designed for feeding orphan puppies (and kittens).

In an emergency, a small needle-less hypodermic syringe or a medicine dropper can be used but with these there is always the danger that the puppy sucks in more air than food. All the proprietary foods carry instructions regarding the approximate quantities necessary to be fed at each meal but as a rough guide the puppy's stomach should be watched and not allowed to become over-distended.

At birth and for the first week feeding every two or three hours is mandatory but provided the puppies are kept in a temperature of around 80°F and the atmosphere is kept moist with a piece of damp cotton wool or damp towels in the box with them, they can quite successfully go through the night between 12 p.m. and 6 a.m. However, it is mandatory that they are kept in a constant temperature and for this purpose an infra red heater is ideal.

When feeding the pup it should be held in a fairly upright position and in this way milk is unlikely to enter the trachea and cause the pup to choke. If the puppy will not feed, do not try to force it. Ask your veterinary surgeon, who may show you how to feed by gavage or stomach tube which as a last resort has been known to save weakly puppies.

After each meal the puppies must be stimulated to urinate and defecate. The bitch normally does this by licking them vigorously and in her absence this can be stimulated by rubbing the puppies along the back and round the perineum (anal region) using a damp piece of cotton wool. It is imperative that this procedure should be carried out after each meal, otherwise alimentary problems will ensue.

Although probably elementary, it must be emphasized that scrupulous cleanliness must be adhered to. Enteric infections in orphan puppies are easily acquired from dirty feeding utensils or a dirty technique adopted during preparation of the food.

Handling and socialisation of these orphan puppies leads to a very strong human/animal bond and they are frequently very much more advanced than puppies reared 'naturally'. Weaning should be commenced as soon as their eyes are open, from about the sixteenth to the eighteenth day. Tip their noses with the feeding bottle so that a little of

---

* Ashe Laboratories   ** Hoechst Ltd.

the formula adheres to their lips. In this way they will soon learn to lap and then their noses can be dipped into a shallow saucer of the same formula. Raw, scrapped meat placed into their mouths soon has them chewing and as soon as this is accomplished you can then try them on one of the proprietary puppy foods.

Foster-mother Although many whelps have been reared by hand from birth in some such way as just outlined, the introduction of a foster-mother and her management must be described, as it will save much time and labour, and bitch's milk is better than any substitute, since it contains many of the antibodies which will protect the puppy against common diseases such as distemper, parvovirus and many of the enteric conditions. Any breed about the same size as the normal dam can be chosen. If she comes with one or two whelps of her own she may prove chary of the strangers. This is overcome by keeping her away from the whelps she has to adopt until the following has been done: if she has any sacking or bedding of her own rub the whelps all over with this; put her whelps with the new ones and rub them together; go to the teats, squeeze out some of her milk and smear this all over the orphans. All this is done with the object of making the whelps new to her smell like her own. This done, she will probably settle down at once and let the orphans suckle from her. If the foster-mother has no whelps of her own smear with her milk those she has to adopt before introducing them.

Cats will often make excellent foster-mothers.

To conclude this section a statement made earlier is repeated—namely that although some rather grim details connected with whelping have had to be given it must be remembered that in the majority of cases the process is an interesting and happy event for the bitch and her owner. As this is not always so, however, every breeder should know what may occur and know how to act if skilled assistance is not immediately available.

Chapter 14

An example of a difficult whelping with complications—
Examples of inexperience

NOTE: The anecdotal incidents described in this chapter will be of little value to the reader today, but their historic interest makes them well worth including in this edition.

A complicated whelping

The reader has now been taken through phases of whelpings, beginning with general principles, passing on to detailed explanation of normal whelpings and finally through a summary of major and minor complications.

The account of an actual whelping case should be of interest, also of value in impressing on the reader the fact that whelping may not always be just the simple biological function he may have imagined it to be.

It would be unwise to confine a book of this kind only to breeds of which the author has had personal experience, so the experience of an authority in another breed has been included.

This case is given pride of place because it is really an amazing one. Its exceptional nature will be obvious to the reader in the light of the knowledge he has now gained.

I am indebted to an eminent breeder of Boxers for permission to tell this story of one of her champion bitches.

The bitch went through the weeks of her pregnancy in a perfectly normal manner; her appetite had been good throughout and she had exercised normally and alone. She had carried her puppies well without any sign of discomfort and had whelped normally, five puppies being born without any great effort, and the bitch appeared to have settled down contentedly in the customary way. The veterinary surgeon thought otherwise, however—and how sound it was that he had wisely been called in for the routine post-whelping examination! He considered that there were still two unborn whelps which were moving down only very slowly. An unbroken vigil was kept during the night but the bitch was comfortable and seemed quite content with the family she had already produced. Temperature was normal, but the veterinary surgeon's examination revealed a lump which could have been a knotted muscle, but which he distrusted. *Five* days later there was a rise in temperature and it was decided to make an X-ray examination, a very sound and necessary course. It revealed nothing. The owner's hopes rose but were dashed when the veterinary surgeon stuck to his original diagnosis, maintaining that the shadow of the ribs could easily be concealing something. Caesarean section was considered, but before resorting to that operation a further effort was made with warm douches, and by further injections of pituitrin to contract the uterus and induce delivery. Penicillin injections had been given every day after the birth of the first five whelps. (Note carefully this fact.) During the fifth night the bitch, being particularly clean in her habits and using only a certain field for her purpose, made several excursions to her particular spot in that field. Next morning, temperature was normal, discharge recurred, and the unusual lump had gone. While the owner and veterinary surgeon were puzzling over the situation another of the owner's bitches appeared on the scene, looking worried and not quite certain whether she was doing the right thing, but obviously feeling that something needed attention. She was carrying in her mouth a dead puppy! One would have thought that this would end the owner's troubles, but the veterinary surgeon was still not satisfied; he did not consider that the uterus was yet quite normal, or completely emptied. Two more days passed with no untoward event, except that the bitch's milk supply failed and the pups had to be hand-fed. The bitch was grateful for this assistance, her chief anxiety being that only one whelp was fed at a time. She moaned quietly to herself about those not yet fed but was quite happy again when the whole family's meal was completed.

On the *seventh* day, and three days after the field birth, temperature rose again and excessive discharge appeared. Pituitrin was again administered, but this time a close watch was kept on the bitch. She was confined to a room and allowed no further visits to her field. During this night the bitch was very sick, and quite suddenly there was an upheaval and a most hideously deformed puppy was delivered, bent over backwards with head and hind feet entangled. It was dead. For a week afterwards there was a continual and very severe haemorrhage, the bitch becoming extremely ill, and only the care of a very clever veterinary surgeon pulled her through.

When the haemorrhage ceased and the discharge had cleared and several days had passed normally, no one could fail to decide that this whelping had, despite its vicissitudes, been satisfactorily concluded. This, however, was not so. A fortnight after the end of this haemorrhage it was seen that tiny bones were being evacuated *via* the vagina. A possibility was that they were from the last deformed puppy, but as so many gradually appeared, and were from all parts of a skeleton, the veterinary surgeon was non-committal. Apparently he thought the whelping was still not yet through.

In actual fact, exactly *four and a half weeks* after the original birth of five puppies a complete leg and an almost unrecognizable head arrived. Pituitrin was again given and a little crushed torso came away; and further anatomical bony parts had to come before all could be assembled into an entire foetus. Not until after seven weeks from the first birth could the owner feel that her worries were really over and that the bitch would survive. The opinion of the veterinary surgeon was that this last puppy had died at about the sixth week of pregnancy, and was the cause of all the trouble. (A condition sufficiently septic to disturb the entire balance of the whelping phenomenon would undoubtedly have been set up.) The surviving puppies proved to be strong and lively, and full of fun and vigour.

The owner very naturally confessed to a thrill of pride in these hand-raised babies and was only too happy to say that the bitch was now looking quite well. In her own words, she regarded her as a living miracle. She was also kind enough to recommend the special diet she had given to the puppies for the first three days after birth. It was: cow's milk and glucodin, then a mixture of slippery elm and glucodin of creamy consistency, gradually thickening, and alternating the glucodin with honey. Added to each feeding bottle were a few drops of rose-hip syrup, a pinch of calcium phosphate and a few drops of cod liver oil. (Many of the constituents of this diet would counteract deficiencies or impurities in what little milk came from the bitch at the very early stage, and would maintain the good start the whelps had made.)

A comment on one word of the owner's narrative. She regards her bitch as a living miracle, and rightly so. She omits, however—doubtless from modesty—to point out that the miracle was due to three factors. First, her knowledge, her unremitting care, and her affection, things for which she deserves the highest praise. Second, the skill of the clever, conscientious veterinary surgeon with whom she co-operated so efficiently. Third, one word—penicillin. Intelligent, knowledgeable owner; painstaking veterinary surgeon; penicillin; in these three complementary elements lies the moral.

How well the story bears out a rule which has been stressed in earlier pages—the absolute necessity of the veterinary surgeon's visit after whelping is *apparently* over. Had there not been one in this case the bitch would undoubtedly have died from a metritis and an acute general septic condition within a few days of the original birth, her milk would have been contaminated before she died, and in all probability the whelps would have been lost too. Instead, the veterinary surgeon attended and penicillin was injected. Dogs react very favourably to penicillin; it is amazing how extreme septic conditions can be controlled and cured by its administration. For four and a half weeks after the original birth there was a putrid, disintegrating, decomposing whelp in the womb, and it was penicillin that prevented a general septicaemia. In the days before penicillin there would not have been a chance of the bitch surviving her gruesome ordeal; one can safely say that the case would have proved fatal within seven days. It is not permissible for an owner to acquire and administer penicillin himself but it is his bounden duty during many aspects of whelping to co-operate with the veterinary surgeon, who can use it in good time.

I have had a similar case in a boxer where a mummified foetus was found in the uterus at routine sterilization fourteen months after successfully raising a litter. T.T.

Examples of inexperience

A further example is given with the object of showing a complete contrast with the first case mentioned so far as care and treatment (or lack of them) are concerned, although the conditions were similar. Comparison between the two results will be inevitable.

A veterinary surgeon had been asked if he could recall the longest period he had known of a bitch producing whelps or foeti after the actual due date of parturition. Since his experience of such a case had been recent he could quite positively say the most protracted case in his memory was three weeks and one day. A bitch was brought to him critically ill, semi-conscious and unable to stand, but very obviously due to whelp. To his horror he received the following history. The puppies had been due three weeks previously. The bitch had seemed quite well, however, and there was no alarm when she produced two live puppies a week later than the due date. Nothing further was done. The puppies died because the bitch 'did not seem to be going on very well', and it was eventually decided to bring her to see him because 'she seemed to be getting worse'.

On examining and palpating the uterus the veterinary surgeon came to the conclusion that there were several whelps in the uterus, obviously dead. If he did not operate the bitch would certainly die in a few hours, whereas if he operated there was a remote chance that she might live.

Operation would involve complete removal of all the organs. It was carried out. The womb contained a conglomerate mass of decomposed, dismembered whelps. The bitch rallied and lived for two days, and although the sepsis was controlled by the immediate injection of penicillin she was so weak that she succumbed to the post-operative shock.

The second object in describing this case is that it will serve as an indictment of cruelty against owners. Censure in this case, however, can be tempered by the fact that the cruelty was due entirely to ignorance, the owner being an amateur with a pet bitch and she thought she would 'like it to have some puppies'. Unfortunately, throughout the country there are many such pet owners with the same thought. Although their motive can be admired, their lack of intelligence or knowledge must be condemned.

Finally, as a contrast, the following has been chosen as the most humorous example of whelping inexperience.

A foreign lady had had a service to her bitch from one of our dogs; she was quite a novice. The author expected that she would be fussy when whelping time came, and a telephone call each evening of the week prior to the event rather proved it. The day the bitch was due to whelp the owner sounded more than unduly anxious, so it was decided to go over and assist her with the whelping. Arriving at 8 p.m. the usual imminent signs were evident but no actual labour. Thereafter till about 2 a.m. the night was punctuated by increasing jitteriness on the owner's part. In the bitch's interest it was tactfully suggested to the owner that she should go into another room and make herself some tea until there was anything to report. The bitch was restless, going to the door and scratching it, and as she had not been let out to relieve herself for some time, the owner was asked to give her a walk in the garden for a few minutes. Shortly after an ear-splitting shriek was heard, loud enough to wake all the neighbours. The author and his wife hurried out and by torchlight perceived the owner at the extreme end of the garden, rooted to the ground. At her feet was the bitch with a whelp just being delivered! As this was not quite the place for the proceedings to continue they side-stepped back to the whelping room, the author carrying the bitch while facing his wife, who was supporting the whelp, the latter being delivered but the cord and placenta still attached to the bitch.

The routine procedure being followed, the whelping was concluded normally. However, the author firmly believes two things. Firstly, that the bitch, having been thoroughly bored with days of undue human fussing over her, had decided that when she was certain that she was going to have her whelps she would get as far away from humans as she could. Secondly, that had he not been present, the owner would have dialled 999 for the Fire Brigade, Police and Ambulance!

Another case of complete inexperience is the one of an owner ringing up her veterinary surgeon in a state of great agitation and informing him that her bitch was having puppies '*via* her mouth'. The veterinary surgeon actually found it difficult to convince her that this could not possibly be the case. Only after he had explained that it was quite normal for a bitch to carry a pup about in her mouth, and resent anyone trying to take it from her, did it dawn on the owner that she had not beheld a whelping miracle. The owners were a married couple with two children, and one would have imagined that they would have had some knowledge of the facts of life—at least enough to know that there is marked similarity between the biological processes of humans and canines. One feels that this bitch might have had a rough time if the whelping had proved difficult ... if the owners were concentrating attention on her mouth!

Another true example of inexperience—that of the lady who quite definitely thought that as her bitch had ten nipples it must invariably have ten pups at each litter, and was quite annoyed when it didn't!

* * *

This book has been written for the amateur pet breeder every bit as much as for the novice breeder exhibitor, who probably already has some knowledge of the subject. Owners of stud dogs in all breeds will undoubtedly have had experience of amateurs bringing pets to be mated, and will have gathered from questions asked that their visitors were ignorant of the fundamentals of the process to which they proposed subjecting their bitch. For many years now the author, after carrying out matings to bitches of amateur owners, has done one of three things: given them a half-hour talk on what to expect before, during and after whelping time, or given them written instructions on the subject, or lent them, or recommended to them, the breed book dealing with the elementaries of whelping. If other genuine dog lovers, including commercialized stud-fee earners, could realize how much suffering would be ended for in-whelp bitches, and to what extent the bitch mortality rate would be lowered, they, too, would give the amateur pet owner guidance, or at least advise him to read a book on whelping. Only a little knowledge, if based on principles, is preferable to the abysmal ignorance which the writer has met far too frequently. The expectant mother and her whelps would silently though most gratefully appreciate the extra attention which intelligent knowledge would substitute for cruel, though ignorant, neglect.

Chapter 15

Disease management—Inoculation—Phantom Pregnancy—Unwanted
Litters
by Trevor Turner B. Vet. Med., MRCVS

Before contemplating having a litter from your bitch there are certain things you must do. Firstly ensure that she has been comprehensively wormed. Today modern worm remedies will cover both tape and round worms and it is worthwhile contacting your veterinary surgeon and discussing this problem with him. He will no doubt not only advise worming before mating but actually during pregnancy; some of the remedies available today are quite safe to administer even late in pregnancy. Both bitch and puppies will then have to be wormed, especially against roundworm, when the puppies are only two or three weeks old and this too has to be repeated on several occasions.

While discussing the proposed mating with your vet, check on the bitch's inoculation status. Has she been fully inoculated? When is a booster due? If she is nearly due for her annual 'top-up' it might be worth having this done a little early to ensure she has the best possible immunity when she goes to visit the stud dog and subsequently when she whelps. The dam's immunity is passed on to the puppies both via the bloodstream and also more importantly by her milk supply and therefore a fully inoculated bitch at whelping is conferring on her puppies the best possible immunity she can.

Today dogs are normally inoculated against distemper, hepatitis (a liver disease) two forms of kidney disease (caused by a leptospiral organism) and also canine parvovirus disease. It is canine parvovirus in recent years that has caused the majority of the headaches with inoculation, since the immunity that puppies receive from their dams can sometimes be relatively long lasting. Until comparatively recently this used to interfere with early inoculation, neutralising any vaccine, so that once the maternal immunity waned, sometimes as late as four or five months of age, the puppy was completely vulnerable. Today the new generation of canine parvovirus vaccines have gone some way to overcoming this problem but the advice of your veterinary surgeon should always be sought regarding conditions in your particular area.

Another class of diseases that must be considered is the so-called inherited and breed pre-disposed diseases. These range from cataract and Progressive Retinal Atrophy (a cause of increasing blindness) to disabling diseases such as Hip Dysplasia. Joint Kennel Club/British Veterinary Association schemes aimed at identifying individual carriers are available for some of the eye conditions and also Hip Dysplasia, conditions which have been recognized in a wide range of breeds. Your veterinary surgeon is the best person to advise. Therefore that pre-mating chat becomes even more worthwhile.

It is not uncommon for bitches after a heat to develop a phantom pregnancy when they, although not in whelp, think they are and will develop milk and adopt a nesting behaviour. Sometimes their whole demeanour will change and they will become aggressive even towards members of the family if they are disturbed. Invariably these animals make splendid mothers but please do not think that mating will be the answer to the bitch's problems. The next time she comes in season her desire for puppies will be even greater and therefore her phantom that much worse, so do not be misled by well-intentioned people who tell you, when you have a bitch in a false pregnancy, to have her mated.

Finally, I would like to say just a few words about mating, pregnancy and whelping in general. As a veterinary surgeon who has owned and bred from bitches of various breeds all his life, I am utterly convinced that dog breeding is a specialized business and should not be entered into lightly by enthusiastic amateurs who feel that it would be nice to have a litter. There are many unwanted dogs in the world today, rescue kennels are full to overflowing, not only with mongrels but with pedigree pets who are 'people mistakes'. Do not add to them! Carefully consider the amount of work and expense that will be involved in rearing a litter of puppies and, last but not least, consider the disposal of those puppies. If there are any doubts that you will not be able to cope, don't join: leave breeding to the specialized breeders!

In practice I frequently hear the story that well-intentioned owners have been told that a 'litter will do the bitch good'. After nearly thirty years in practice I have still to find this bitch that 'has been done good'. A pet bitch, suddenly presented with a family of her own is frequently confused and torn between her desire to be with her proper family with whom she has grown up and her instinctive urge to be with her natural family. If she normally sleeps in the owner's bedroom and has suddenly been relegated to the kitchen because she has a litter of puppies, she cannot reconcile this and will not settle, carrying puppies from pillar to post. This is upsetting for all concerned, not least the puppies. At the end of the day there is the question of disposal. All those people who enthusiastically wanted a puppy at the time of whelping suddenly find

114

a multiplicity of plausible reasons why they don't want one of the pups and so the problems mount.

Think carefully before you add to the cohort of unwanted puppies. Do not think however that I am opposed to anyone with a pet bitch breeding from her. On the contrary, many of the top exhibitors and breeders in this country today started in just that way. All I am emphasizing is that you should carefully consider your circumstances. Have you the time, the facilities, the market; above all, the energy and enthusiasm? If the answer to all or most of these questions is 'Yes' you will find that those established within your breed and not least your veterinary surgeon will do all they can to help.

Good luck.

Index